# CALL TO COURAGE

# Call to Courage

*A Story of Mother Theodore Guérin*

*by*

SISTER JOSEPH ELEANOR, S.P.

*Illustrated by*
*Carolyn Lee Jagodits*

DUJARIE PRESS / NOTRE DAME

*Nihil Obstat:* *John P. Lynch, C.S.C., Censor Deputatus*
*Imprimatur:* *Leo A. Pursley, D.D., Bishop of Fort Wayne-South Bend*

Library of Congress Catalog Card Number: 68-23381

The author wishes to express grateful acknowledgment of the community research made available, especially that of Sister Eugenia Logan, S.P., who in addition to reading the manuscript, offered invaluable advice and encouragement.

# CONTENTS

# A Girl in Brittany

**1**    "Anne-Thérèse, my dear, where did you get that?" Madame Guérin rose from the table, book in hand, as her eight-year-old daughter appeared for her lesson crowned with a dainty, old-fashioned cap.

Anne-Thérèse's dark eyes danced. "In the trunk upstairs, *Maman!* We were dressing up, you know. I shall wear it when I take Marie-Jeanne out for her walk today."

Anne-Thérèse stood on tiptoe to admire herself in the shiny bottom of one of the pans hanging from the wall in the homey Breton kitchen. As she did so, she saw something else reflected—her mother's slender hand reaching out to lift the cap from her head.

She looked up. "*Maman*, what is wrong? You are crying! What is the matter, *Maman?* Have I done something wrong?"

Madame Guérin's arm went around her little girl and hugged her hard. "No, dear; but you will not wear this out with Marie-Jeanne, Thérèse. We'll put it back where you found it, and I shall put away the key to that trunk!"

"But why, *Maman?*"

Madame Guérin looked for a moment down at Anne-Thérèse's eager face, and then over the child's head out the broad window towards the sea. Then she smiled suddenly.

"Why? Well, that shall be your history lesson for today. Come, sit down, now." Madame Guérin herself sat down again at the table, looking down at the little cap she held folded in her hands as though it were a page of history she was reading to her little daughter.

"This brings back memories to me, Anne-Thérèse, but I myself have never worn it, and neither must you, my dear. It's . . ."

"Is it a relic, *Maman?*"

"A relic? Well, in a way I suppose it is. You see, *chérie*, long ago, before you were even thought of, things were different in our beloved France."

"You mean like Charlemagne and the knights, *Maman?*"

"Well, in a way like Charlemagne and the knights. Really, I suppose our story does go that far back. The great castles that you like to think about, my Anne-Thérèse, and the great deeds you like to dream of, go back to those times when the knights had to build fortresses for protection, and the poorer and weaker pledged their services to those who could help and defend them. And so a situation came about which brought many problems to be faced through the centuries. You will learn much about it, Anne-Thérèse, as you study your history lessons."

Madame Guérin, like other mothers of her time, had herself undertaken the education of her children. Born before the Revolution, of a well-to-do family of the lesser nobility, she had been well educated; and she enjoyed teaching her little ones the truths of their faith, the lessons of Scripture, the elements of language, mathematics, and, of course, history. It was a pleasure to teach Anne-Thérèse, for the child was alert, lively, precocious.

Now she went on. "Some of the most terrible of those problems, my dear, had to be faced by the people of the past century, the century in which your father and I grew up. We still had a king then, King Louis XVI, and a beautiful queen. We still had beautiful monasteries and convents, noble bishops, curés in every village. There were monks and nuns to care for the sick and poor. Wealthy noble ladies shared their time and goods in charity, and in the great houses there were balls and festivities, in many of them learning

[ 10 ]

and culture. Life in France had a pleasant side.

"But there were still the weak and the poor, growing every year weaker and poorer, and ever more restless. For although many of the nobility did what they could to help the lower classes, it was not charity, really, that these people needed, but justice. You see, Anne-Thérèse, there were many rich nobles who in heedlessness and greed thought only of what they might get and spend, only of their own comfort and pleasure, and nothing of their neighbor.

"Meantime, the people, seeing what those in other lands had done—our own generals helped the brave Americans win their freedom from oppression—thought that the time had come for them to see what they might do."

"I should think they would go to the king," declared Anne-Thérèse.

"Of course. And so they did."

"Why didn't he do something? Wasn't he a good king?"

"King Louis was very good, but unfortunately he was not very energetic or farseeing. Had he been, things might have turned out far otherwise! As it was, our Estates-General met, ten years before you were born, Anne-Thérèse, and many things began to happen. First of all, the old feudal system was abolished. Then," Madame Guérin's gaze seemed very far away, "then, they did away with the king, and finally had him, and his queen, and thousands of nobles, sent to the guillotine. Yes, thousands of aristocrats and thousands of priests."

"Priests, *Maman*? What did they do wrong?"

"It was not always necessary, in those years, to do something wrong, Anne-Thérèse. Even to be suspected of not siding with the party in power at the time was to risk death. But you see, my dear, back in that fateful year of 1789, a law had been passed permitting the government to take over all Church lands. That law was soon followed by others which did away with monasteries and convents, even religious vows. All the clergy were to be under the control of the new state, and to make sure of this, when many objected, the priests and bishops were obliged to take an oath in support of the new arrangements."

"But they wouldn't do it!" interrupted Anne-Thérèse. "I am sure I wouldn't do it, if I thought it was wrong. Nobody would make me do something I thought was wrong!"

From what she had already observed of her elder daughter, Madame Guérin was quite ready to believe that no one would make her do something she thought wrong. Also, it would be very hard to prevent her from doing something she thought right, or necessary. She drew the indignant little form closer to her.

"There were very many who thought just like that, Anne-Thérèse, and that is why many priests were condemned to the guillotine, or imprisoned, or sent out of the country."

"Sent out of France! That would be worse than being in prison!" While the truly French Anne-Thérèse pondered the dismal prospects of people forced to leave France, Madame Guérin recalled the painful years of the past decade. Whole districts had been deprived of the benefits of their religion. Forbidden to enter the churches or perform religious services, the loyal clergy had no regular homes or duties. In order to serve their people they had to work at night, in secret, like vagabonds frequently changing abode. There were no religious schools; Mass was celebrated in homes, in the fields, in barns. Often it was a relative or a friend who baptized a newborn child, when no priest could be found.

Such had been the conditions in the closing year of the century when Anne-Thérèse was born. Things looked a little better now that Napoleon had come into power and promised to bring about some sort of order —if only he could keep out of more foreign wars, and curb his ambition.

Madame Guérin looked down at the little cap in her hands. It was a graceful symbol of the old nobility to which Anne-Thérèse's great-grandmother, Gabrielle Louays de la Cour, who once wore it, had belonged; but the rights of that nobility had passed away. A new nobility was needed, one of more faith and courage. She smoothed her small daughter's hair. "That will be enough lessons for today, I think, *chérie*. Put on your shawl and go out for a while. But not far, now!"

Anne-Thérèse needed no second invitation to go free for a time; still, her small steps were not quite so light as usual, and she wore a thoughtful expression as she closed the door behind her and took the path towards the sea.

Madame Guérin stood at the window watching her. A short distance away sparkled the sea, alive with small fishing boats that bobbed and danced in its waves, beneath a sky that was piercingly clear and blue. Sea and sky together seemed an endless expanse. The words of an old Breton fisherman's prayer came to Madame Guérin's mind, "May God protect us, for the sea is so big, and our ships are so little."

There was a firm step across the threshold and suddenly her husband was beside her.

"Laurent! You startled me!" A smile softened the reproach.

"I have been watching you." It was his turn to smile. "Your eyes have been on the sea, and your thoughts on the little one, isn't that so?"

"You are too clever at reading my thoughts, my dear!"

"That's because we think alike. And a good thing, too!" Laurent Guérin's hand closed over the slim hand holding the little white cap. His wife knew well what he meant. Both were of good families, and both were now more or less in the bad graces of their families as a result of the political dissensions of the times. Madame Guérin's family, the Lefèvre, were staunch royalists and frowned upon her marriage into a family which favored the rising Napoleon. Laurent's family, on the other hand, could not countenance an alliance between their son and a royalist. Many of their former friends and acquaintances shared the family opinions.

Of course, the attitude of family and friends had only drawn the young couple closer together. They had each other, their home, and their children. What more could they want?

"Yes, it is a good thing, Laurent," echoed Isabelle. "God has been very good to us. What more could we ask?"

Again and again over the years they had asked each other this question, often in joy, sometimes in bitter sorrow. For sorrow had come early to the little home by the sea. Of their four children, the two boys had been taken by death in early childhood—one in a tragic fire at the age of three. Anne-Thérèse and Marie-Jeanne, six years younger, alone remained to be doubly cherished.

As the parents watched, the small form of Anne-Thérèse turned and began to approach the house. She had remembered her promise to take the baby out. The serious thoughts her mother had aroused had made her forget, but only for a time. Anne-Thérèse began to skip as she hurried up the path.

## An Officer's Daughter

**2** Brittany is an old and rugged land, a land of legend and romance. Poised at the very western tip of France, it looks out over the Atlantic towards the New World from steep crags and broad fields dotted with the relics of centuries. In Brittany, before the time of Christ, the Druids held their festivals; there the Roman conquerors built their roads and towns; there in early Christian times the Celtic monks erected monasteries and cathedrals, and kindled the faith that still sings out from wayside shrines and calvaries.

It is a land almost surrounded by the sea. Against its rocky coast white billows break, and from its busy ports set out the little fishing boats manned by sturdy Breton seamen. Everything about the land and its inhabitants speaks of strength, of endurance, and of high ideals.

There had indeed been need of all these qualities during the past ten years. As the century closed, not only pagan and Roman, but Christian and medieval ruins attested to the ravages of war and revolution, even here in Brittany. Here, too, abandoned monasteries, desolate churches, ignorance and destitution cried out for courageous, high-souled laborers. But no one in the Guérin home, least of all Anne-Thérèse, had any idea of the share that she would have in the great works being prepared.

She continued to enjoy her mother's lessons, and she enjoyed, although not quite so much, the time she spent, when she was nine, as pupil of a zealous young woman who tried to form a little school in her own home. Perhaps what Anne-Thérèse liked best about this school was the opportunity it gave her to exercise her leadership among little companions just as old, but not quite so advanced as Madame Guérin's lessons had made her daughter. Even so, there were times when boredom overcame her and she managed a stolen free day in the fields while slower pupils struggled with their books.

She was not at all disappointed when the little school closed, especially since something quite unexpected and exciting soon happened. A distant relative, forced to discontinue for a time his studies for the priesthood, arrived in Étables. Promptly he offered his services as private tutor; and since he was both interested and able, and Anne-Thérèse only too ready to learn, she quickly acquired a fine background for her future career. Rhetoric, Latin, more Scripture, more history, more mathematics. Mlle. Guérin was being very well prepared for the future. She loved it. It made her feel quite grown-up and special to have a tutor all to herself.

But more, perhaps, than her studies, Anne-Thérèse loved the sea. She loved to slip down to the shore, down to where the water met white sand, and seated on one of the gray rocks, to look out and listen, while the water lapped her sabots, and the wind blew back the wings of her stiff white cap, and the sea told her many things. She could not remember a time when she had not delighted to listen to the waves, wondering what lay beyond.

After all, it was only natural that she should love the sea; she was very much her father's daughter. And Captain Guérin was a naval officer. More and more his family was becoming aware of this, as Napoleonic campaigns took him away from home.

The story of France in the ten years after Anne-Thérèse's birth is the story of Napoleon's triumphs. Once in power, he went on from victory to victory until by 1810 he dominated Europe. He had even arrested and imprisoned the pope. One after another, he placed members of his family and his friends at the head of conquered states. But when he appointed his brother Joseph king in Spain, the Spanish people protested, and Laurent Guérin was one of the French naval officers ordered to accompany the emperor into Spain to protect his threatened interests. Anne-Thérèse was not yet twelve when her father left.

The little family had never grown used to saying good-bye, and this time it seemed even harder. Anne-Thérèse looked with concern at her mother's face as Madame Guérin gazed into the distance long after Captain Guérin had disappeared from view. As she put her arms around her mother's waist, she felt her trembling.

"Don't feel sad, *Maman chérie*," she whispered.

"God will take care of him. He always has."

Madame Guérin shook her head. "Somehow I never felt like this before." If in her heart she thought, "Oh, why did he have to follow the Corsican?" she did not say it aloud. The Corsican was now the leader of France, and Laurent was only doing, as always, his patriotic duty. She added quietly, "But you are right, Thérèse. God will surely take care of him."

Meantime, Anne-Thérèse resolved she would do her best to help. She kept herself busy with housework and with her garden, with extra little attentions to her mother and big-sisterly supervision of Marie-Jeanne. Madame Guérin had already discovered that her elder daughter possessed a very fine business sense and was growing into a splendid little manager. What a capable, efficient little person she is, thought the mother affectionately. More and more she found herself relying on Anne-Thérèse.

## By the Bridge of Avignon

**3** If the little family in Étables found the two years of Captain Guérin's absence long, the captain himself found them almost endless. Only rarely could he write, and then he could not be sure his letters would reach their destination. In an enemy land, surrounded by a populace rightfully resentful of his own country's aggression, he and his brother officers found their one consolation, as fighting men always must, in dreams of what might be "after the war."

Events were not favoring Napoleon. Fighting in defense of their own homes, the Spaniards had shown what patriotism can do even against superior forces. The city of Saragossa had successfully resisted a besieging army, and Napoleon's brother Joseph had withdrawn from Madrid. It was time for the emperor to become seriously disturbed. He decided to strengthen his blockade of the Mediterranean.

Captain Guérin was serving in the naval detachment which patrolled this sea between Spain and Africa. Sometimes as he stood on deck on a clear bright day, his gaze sought out the coast of France far to the north of the fleet. The Romans had called this great blue expanse "our sea." If Napoleon had his way, perhaps another nation might be doing the same.

But Napoleon was just now meeting with increasing opposition and so for a time had to change his plans. Captain Guérin was spending his leisure on deck one evening when a fellow officer excitedly approached him.

"Did you hear, Captain," he exclaimed, "the emperor is going to move against Alexander!"

"Against Russia?"

"But yes, all things considered, I suppose it will be necessary for him. And I hear we, too, are to go. At least that is the rumor."

"I had hoped for a furlough. I have one due."

"I also, Captain. Let us hope, both of us!"

Their hopes were realized. Napoleon was returning to France before his campaign; Captain Guérin and his companions easily obtained the furlough they sought. They made joyful preparations to spend some time at home before setting out for the long, hard Russian drive. Finally, fortified by full pay and eager anticipations, they arrived at Toulon.

Once on land, Captain Guérin dispatched the happy news to his family and cast about for the quickest way home. Hearing that a party was leaving Avignon for Brittany, he left his other companions at Toulon and set out alone to join this group.

Avignon, famous city of song and story, scene for so long of papal captivity, stood in the glowing southern sun as an eloquent symbol of the relations between

Church and State in the France to which Captain Guérin was returning. Pope Pius VII was still Napoleon's prisoner. But just now speculations as to how this situation might end could not dull the captain's happiness at the thought of seeing his family once again. He strode on purposefully, steadily, stopping only when sheer exhaustion forced him to take rest in a little inn.

He was not alone in the tiny, close dining room. Seated at the table were a motley trio already in earnest conversation. One was a tall, slender man with an inexpressibly sad expression; he contemplated a dish of soup as though it held the answers to all the problems of the world. Near him sat a stocky, dark-skinned man who might have been either a mule driver or a road mender, so dusty were his clothes. A wiry young man with a dirty red bandanna circling a head of bristling red hair completed the group. He was amusing himself by walking his fingers up and down the checks in the tablecloth when Captain Guérin entered.

Ordinarily Laurent Guérin's shy courtesy made him reserved, even distant, with strangers. Today his joy at being in France again, on his way to Isabelle and the children, somehow weakened his native Breton caution. He was affable and friendly towards his tablemates, commented on the roads, on the war.

Across the table the lean, sallow fellow lifted his melancholy gaze from his soup plate. "The captain has a long way to go?" he asked.

"Now I certainly hope not," put in the dusty one.

"And why not, if one is permitted to ask?"

"To go far, one would need much money, and in these days, those who have the money to go far have less chance of getting there."

The red-crowned youth kept on walking his fingers.

"That's right, what you say!" The lean man's melancholy visage seemed to lighten a shade. It even threatened to smile. "You are very clever at saying

[ 19 ]

things straight out. But Monsieur doesn't seem to understand!"

Captain Guérin found himself facing three varieties of amused leer. Suddenly uneasy, he realized that he did, indeed, understand. "I have heard of many highway robberies," he ventured. "I thought perhaps order was being restored now."

"Oh yes. But still it's always safer not to go alone. Now if Monsieur is going our way . . ."

But Monsieur suddenly decided that he would rather risk going alone. Shortly excusing himself, he went to his room, resolved to set out very early in the morning, before the ill-favored three had rested from the carouse with which they would undoubtedly end the night.

So he started out before sunrise, all the quickened anticipation of his soul reflected in the spreading glory of mauve and rose, of saffron and gold in the sky before him. The city of Avignon was just awaking as he approached. Here and there footsteps clicked in the quiet streets; the first rumble of cart wheels sounded on the other side of the bridge.

But Captain Guérin was not to cross that bridge. As he strode along, savoring his happy dreams, he saw too late a flash of red flare up from the dusty bushes beside the road. It was followed at once by two other vaulting forms; the next instant the captain was surrounded. In vain he offered all his money for his life. His assailants, the tablemates of the previous night, seized his purse and dashed away, leaving him lifeless beside the road.

Later that day a little group moved on from Avignon, unaware that one member was missing from their ranks.

\* \* \*

While these events were taking place near France's southern coast, in a little village near the sea that washed its western shores there was delicious excitement.

*"Maman,* look! Anne-Thérèse! A messenger! Oh, it is from papa, I know it is!" It was Marie-Jeanne, now nearly eight years old, who first saw the messenger coming up the pebbled lane, and who danced in eagerness while her mother opened the dispatch. Anne-Thérèse, now almost fourteen, watched her mother's face with tremulous concern. But the tears she saw there were tears of joy, and through the mist in her own eyes the girl read the announcement that trembled in her mother's hand. He was coming home at last!

With steps that fairly flashed, the three set about joyful preparations for his return. There was a wonderful sweeping and swishing, and airing and polishing, a routing of dust that the returning wayfarer would never see anyway, having eyes only for his dear ones. There was assessment of stores and planning of tasty menus. There was rehearsal of things to be said; there were dreams of things to be done.

And, as the days went by, there was much earnest gazing down the road, much scanning of the horizon.

But he did not come. Day after day, with dwindling spirits, they went over the house, replanned the meals, watched and waited and prayed. It was well over a year before the news finally reached them which put an end to all hope.

It seemed for a time that Madame Guérin would not survive this heartbreak. Never strong, she faced almost entire collapse. Anne-Thérèse found herself assuming complete control of the little household. It was she who nursed the invalid mother, she who taught and cared for the little sister, she who had to earn their bread and manage their small finances.

So fully did all this occupy her time and tax her resources, that the vague plans for the future, the secret dreams she had cherished from the time of her First Communion five years before, had to be put for the time well out of mind.

[ 21 ]

# Maidens' Dreams

**4** The few years after her father's death were years of trial for Anne-Thérèse. It was hard to see her mother's suffering without being able to remove its cause. Laurent Guérin had been there to help his wife weather the grief of earlier losses, but try as her two daughters might, and did, nothing could fill the emptiness left by his death.

Anne-Thérèse had learned early not to spare herself. Always energetic, purposeful, vivacious, she now spent all her efforts for the two she loved. But the very qualities that made her indispensable to her mother and sister indicated that someday these two must learn to do without her. It was inevitable that such a spirit as hers should have a work to do, a place to fill. Always deep in her heart Anne-Thérèse felt that this was so. Sometimes she was painfully aware of it. She must give herself more fully, belong to God more completely, of that she was sure. As far as she could see, for her there was but one way to do this; she must be a nun. It might break her heart to leave her mother and sister, but there were others, she felt, who needed her, too. Marie-Jeanne was growing up. She could take care of their mother; she should not be deprived of the chance. And besides, Madame Guérin was improving in health.

With such thoughts weaving themselves about in her mind, it was not perhaps strange that Anne-Thérèse was surprised one day into a startling declaration. On their way from a shopping expedition, she and Marie-Jeanne came upon a group of their friends, lively girls, brightly beribboned, clutching gay bonnets in the wind and chattering excitedly. Anne-Thérèse and Marie-Jeanne had to stop to hear the news. Annette was engaged! Starry-eyed, she was receiving the congratulations of her friends.

"You are fortunate, Annette," exclaimed Pauline. "Jean will surely make his way in the world. You'll be living in comfort and style."

"And he's so handsome!"

"And so thoughtful!"

The tiny, dark Annette rapturously agreed with every comment. "Oh, I hope you all find a husband just like Jean—or as like as can be!"

"I suppose you think there can be only one Jean," teased Pauline. "Wait, *chérie*, until you've seen my Robert!"

"Pauline—no!" And then there were more happy exclamations, and Pauline had some difficult moments trying to assure her friends that she was not really engaged. "But truly," she finally declared, "when I do wed, I shall wed a man of wealth, of that you may be sure!"

"I want a husband of culture. One of the old nobility." This from Yvonne.

"And I an officer!"

Anne-Thérèse was enjoying the gay confidences more as an observer than as a participant; for the responsibility she had borne made her seem older than her years, and she was not accustomed to her full share of girlish recreations. Suddenly she found herself the center of attention. "And you, Mademoiselle," demanded Annette. "What about you?"

"I?"

"Yes. Whom shall you choose?"

Coming back from her thoughts, Anne-Thérèse laughed lightly. "Oh," she exclaimed, "my spouse shall be a king!"

"A king! Oho, you *are* ambitious! Who would have thought it?"

"A king? Anne-Thérèse, you surprise me. I had always pictured you as a nun!" Pauline stopped in

[ 23 ]

embarrassment. Fortunately at that moment the appearance of Yvonne's brother and a friend distracted the animated little group. Anne-Thérèse saved herself by hurrying off at such a pace that Marie-Jeanne came breathless behind her.

"Whatever did you mean, Anne-Thérèse?" demanded her sister.

"Mother will be worried if we aren't home. We should not have lingered so long. Come on, Marie-Jeanne." And they hurried home.

It was not to be expected, however, that Marie-Jeanne should forget the incident; nor that she should not seize the first opportunity to regale her mother with an account of the afternoon's adventures; nor yet that Madame Guérin should not question her elder daughter.

"What Marie-Jeanne tells me does not sound like you, Anne-Thérèse," she began, when they sat alone that evening.

"I was really surprised myself," confessed Anne-Thérèse, "but after all, Mother, it is true!" It was a relief to be able to discuss her future with her mother at last.

"True that you have ambitions to wed a king? I am sure you have more sense, Anne-Thérèse!"

"But Mother, I thought surely you would understand. You know the only king I could have been thinking of! Mother, surely you have guessed that I . . . that I want to give my life to Christ!"

"To be a nun!"

Anne-Thérèse winced at her mother's tone. And then she found herself trying to stem the flood of her mother's tears. "How can you be so selfish, Anne-Thérèse? How can you think of going off and leaving me in my condition? Really, I did not expect this of you! I have counted so much on you, Anne-Thérèse!"

"But Mother, Marie-Jeanne . . ."

"Marie-Jeanne is a little scatterbrain. You know she could never manage!"

[ 24 ]

"Perhaps she needs a chance, *Maman.*"

"That will do, Anne-Thérèse. Please help me to bed now. This excitement has quite unnerved me!"

"Yes, Mother." Anne-Thérèse slept little that night, after she had calmed and comforted her mother and evaded her sister's queries.

The following weeks were laced with unpleasantness. Anne-Thérèse's declaration had caused a sensation among her friends; and she often found her little sister looking at her curiously. Then there was her mother's attitude, the hardest to bear. Whenever Madame Guérin adverted to her daughter's desire, there was sure to be a spell of weeping, then reproachful reminders of the many promising suitors whom the girl had let go unheeded. Would it not be better to marry and make a home near her mother? And then there was the age-old argument that one can serve the world better in it than out of it. "What good can you do if you bury yourself in a cloister? You who are so energetic and active?"

Madame Guérin's opposition to her daughter's vocation was not entirely selfish. Deep in her motherly heart was a core of fear lest the girl attempt a life of abnegation and austerity beyond her strength. She had heard Anne-Thérèse speak frequently of Carmel, the order of her patroness; and she more than suspected that the girl was already trying some of its practices under the delusion that she was unobserved.

So she continued her resistance, while long months passed. When Anne-Thérèse's only human support, her confessor, was transferred to another parish, the young girl redoubled her prayers to her heavenly allies. There was the good St. Anne, and there was the great St. Teresa; there were the Guardian Angels, to whom she had always a special devotion, having been born on their feast; above all, there was Our Lady, to whom she had been dedicated from birth. Anne-Thérèse was nearing twenty-five when their answer finally came.

She was kneeling past her usual time one night before Our Lady's statue in her bedroom. Suddenly the door behind her opened, and a soft voice whispered, "Anne-Thérèse, not yet in bed?"

"I have just been praying, Mother." Anne-Thérèse rose, uneasy and embarrassed. Was she making matters worse? But her mother's expression reassured her.

"Oh, my dear," exclaimed Madame Guérin, "I can hold out no longer! I cannot continue to refuse the sacrifice God asks of me. Go, my daughter, with your mother's blessing. But . . . oh, I shall miss you, Anne-Thérèse!"

## A Helping Hand

**5** While Napoleon's fighting men were setting off by land and sea to reinforce his threatened empire, a greater work of reclamation was going on steadily and quietly in the villages and towns of France. The concordat with the pope, signed in 1801, had made it possible for the loyal clergy once again to take up openly duties so long forbidden them; they set themselves earnestly to repairing the harm done by years of destruction and indifference.

And so it happened that one Sunday in May, 1803, the congregation of the parish church at Ruillé-sur-Loir looked up confidently at their new pastor. Father James Dujarié was not a stranger to them. For the past six years he had been here and there among them, visiting the sick at night, saying Mass in a barn or garret, teaching, baptizing, assisting the dying, aiding in every way possible the zealous Abbé Delahaye from his hidden quarters near Ruillé.

He had had a hard apprenticeship, this new pastor; he had proved himself well. Few of his parishioners could not recount some tale of heroic dedication. Even as a seminarian, had he not been one of the faithful ten who would not follow the Civil Clergy? Hadn't he exiled himself from his own family to protect them from suspicion, and tramped the roads, pack over shoulder, peddling linen and other wares? Hadn't he lived hidden in a cellar weaving cloth? Hadn't he said his first Mass in a farmhouse basement, in the dark of a midwinter night? And then lived as best he could, always evading pursuit?

Men from the farm of Fosse-Garnier nodded wisely. Their master, Monsieur Aubry, all during the days of persecution had harbored sometimes as many as four loyal priests at a time. They could tell many a story.

And then there was Pierre, the friend of Monsieur Dufour, captain of police at Chateau-du-Loir. The captain had always been careful to send Pierre on ahead when he himself was due for an official visit of investigation; that way there were sure to be no priests in evidence. Pierre watched the new pastor bless his congregation. It was different now from the night the young *abbé* had scrambled under the hay in the Aubrys' barn, or hidden in the bottom of the Pinaudiers' wagon as it rumbled across the fields towards the home of a sick parishioner.

In the rear of the church, Pierre got down on his knees. Father Dujarié was finishing Mass; somehow Pierre had to blink hard in order to see him clearly.

* * *

The first concern of the new pastor was to arrange for the instruction of the children deprived for so long of religious teaching. After the experiences of the Revolution and the Directory, he felt, it was not surprising that there was indifference, even hostility, towards the faith. And hand in hand with ignorance and ill will in many cases went poverty, even destitution. There was a prodigious task ahead. Father Dujarié started out immediately, begging from door to door, asking for alms, asking for prayers, asking for personal assistance; and within the next two years there was a change in the atmosphere of the parish. People began to contribute what they could. Then one day two generous parishioners, whose names no one seems to know, presented themselves to their pastor.

"We do not know much ourselves," they told him, "but we are willing to learn, and we do want to help."

Father Dujarié was delighted. "Can you teach the catechism?" he asked.

"Oh yes, if you will explain any questions that come up!"

He nodded. "And would you be willing to visit the sick?" Indeed they would! They were true Christian women.

"We might help care for the sick in their homes, and manage the children when their mothers are unable, and otherwise be a help to the poor."

"And you — how will you live? Who will take care of you?"

"All we ask is the good will of the people, and a share of such food and clothing and lodging as is given to them."

"May God reward you!" With kindled eyes, Father Dujarié saw his dream taking shape. "We will be a true Providence to these people, my friends," he exclaimed. "Let us begin at once!"

He began by looking around for a dwelling for his new helpers. Soon, at the corners of paths and lanes, along the borders of the fields, there appeared a new kind of crop: little heaps of stones which the children gathered from fields or woods. There was always a friendly farmer to pick these stones up in his cart and take them to the edge of the village, where Father Dujarié and willing neighbors were building a little home. Finally it was completed, a sturdy dwelling, all of stone and roofed with tile. There were two windows and a door; downstairs there were a kitchen and a schoolroom, above, a garret to serve as dormitory, where in the winter the snow blanketed the beds. They called it "Little Providence."

From this little center workers in gradually increasing numbers went out over the countryside and into the neighboring parishes to teach, to nurse, to advise, to console. Of course, there were never enough laborers for all the work to be done, and the laborers often went hungry and cold; but their austere and unselfish lives and their never-failing charity inspired the confidence of the people and slowly attracted other courageous souls.

Among these recruits was a cultivated, refined, and noble young woman, Mlle. Joséphine Zoé du Roscoät, daughter of the Count Casimir Rolland du Roscoät, a distinguished Breton nobleman who had been forced to emigrate and had lost all his estates during the Revolution. To help her temporarily impoverished family, Mlle. du Roscoät had taken some pupils. When family circumstances improved, she continued her teaching as a work of zeal. For six years she conducted a little school at Saint-Brieuc, devoting her free time to visiting the sick. Then, during a retreat in 1816, she met the Jesuit Father de la Chapelle, to whom she confided her desire to consecrate her life more completely to God and thus to be still more a help to souls in need.

"My child," he said, "God wants you at Ruillé-sur-Loir." And he told her of Father Dujarié's little congregation, already doing so much good. Mlle. du Roscoät immediately applied at Ruillé and was received by Father Dujarié; in a very short time, as Mother Marie Madeleine, she was chosen superior. It was she who helped establish the little group as a true religious community, to be called "Sisters of Providence," and to devote themselves, under rules formulated by Father Dujarié and Father de la Chapelle, to the service of God among children and the needy.

To this community Anne-Thérèse Guérin applied when finally she had obtained her mother's permission.

# New Beginnings

**6** "The new postulant from Étables seems very promising," remarked Sister St. Charles one evening shortly after Anne-Thérèse's entrance in the fall of 1823.

"If she continues as she has begun, she will do much good," agreed Mother Mary. "I find her quite docile and obedient, though she is a little older than the other novices. Then, too, she has had practical experience — and she has good sense."

"And she has learned to accept trials. Just now, however, Mother, I think she is undergoing a very bitter trial — that of homesickness. Oh, she hasn't said anything about it, but I can sense just how she feels, and I can see the signs!"

"Yes, I am afraid she is lonesome; but she will weather that storm. I have great hopes for her, Sister." Mother Mary was a strict novice-mistress. Very demanding of herself, she was demanding of others, too, especially when she saw promise of greatness of soul and generous service. This was true in the case of Anne-Thérèse, who besides shared her background and ancestry; for Mother Mary, too, was a Breton sailor's daughter.

So great, indeed, were her hopes for Anne-Thérèse that even when a severe illness early in her novitiate left the young Sister's health permanently impaired, Mother Mary did not hesitate to let her continue her preparations for the religious life. Anne-Thérèse profited by the long hours of her illness to reflect and pray; by her docility and cheerfulness she proved herself a good patient as well as a good novice; but her frail appearance even after she left the infirmary caused Mother Mary much concern.

One day she called the novice to her room. "Sit down, Sister," she invited, looking solicitously at Anne-Thérèse's wan face. "I have a little news for you. We are going to let you do some missionary work. You are to go with the Sisters who leave for Pruilly this week. I am sure the invigorating climate there will put some color in your cheeks and send you back to us strong and well."

Mother Mary was not mistaken. When Anne-Thérèse returned to Ruillé in September to make the retreat, she seemed indeed improved in health. She had enriched her experience, too, and had grown in the respect of the other Sisters. With contentment and joy she began her retreat — eight days of quiet prayer, of instructions on the religious life, of meditations on the life of Christ and the duties of a Christian, especially a religious, and of careful planning for the future. At the close of the retreat, she was permitted to pronounce her vows as Sister Theodore.

When, after the ceremonies, the Sisters learned their assignments for the coming year, Sister Theodore received a big surprise. She was going to Rennes; she, just professed, was going to just about the hardest place any Sister could be sent. Sister Theodore found herself somewhat distracted during the feast-day dinner and the gay recreation of the afternoon.

The school at Rennes was located in a district inhabited by an unusually neglected and depraved population. People from other sections of the city avoided this area, or passed through only at the risk of insult or assault. When the school had been opened in 1822, the Sisters, realizing the good that might be done, had consented to take charge. Thus far their efforts seemed fruitless. The courses had been planned to help underprivileged, almost abandoned children—simple religious instruction and handicrafts; but these little ones seemed incorrigible.

"It is a difficult mission," Mother Mary told Sister Theodore that afternoon. "But with God's help you will succeed. The bishop is eager to see these poor people receive some knowledge of God, some moral instruction; and he is depending on us. They are really like the heathen. So it is a missionary work we are assigning you, Sister. But," she added, "you will need all your courage!"

"I shall try to justify your confidence in me," Sister Theodore faltered.

"You will certainly have our fervent prayers, Sister. The mission at Rennes is very dear to us. So much good can be accomplished there, but much suffering will have to be borne, too."

Sister Theodore was not afraid of suffering, and she had more than her share of courage. With Mother Mary's blessing, she set off the next day for her new mission.

The children at Rennes were not at all surprised to see a new Sister in charge. They had watched a succession of instructors replace one another. "Here is another one," they thought. "Well, she is going to learn something from us!"

With a clatter of clumsy shoes and much twisting of little bodies, they took their seats, eyes all the while on the new teacher. Beneath each tousled head and impudent smirk was the impish resolution, "We'll show her! It won't take us long to make this one, too, sorry that she came!" They were slow in assembling, and as noisy as possible. Sister Theodore stood before them, slender, dark-eyed, grave. Her heart quaked; she stopped to say a fervent little prayer before she advanced to address them.

Her words were useless. A dark-eyed, black-haired, ragged little miss in the front row jumped up and pointed at her. "Look at her!" she cried to her companions. "She thinks she is going to make us all like Sisters!" At that, everyone laughed—everyone except Sister Theodore.

"Children," she began again; but they laughed all the louder. Sister Theodore stepped to the door, very quietly. Outside in the hall the sewing teacher waited, breathless and quaking. Sister Theodore beckoned to her. Together the Sisters approached the desk, gently they laid out some work, and then Sister Theodore, with a smile and a nod to the noisy little rebels, left the room. The last thing she heard as she went down the hall towards the next classroom was a riotous clamor for materials alternating with the soothing tones of the Sister's voice.

But Sister Theodore was by no means defeated. If present methods failed, some better plans must be made. It was at this time that she adopted a plan she was to continue all her life and recommend to others: whenever she needed help in governing her pupils or touching their hearts, she would appeal for help to their Guardian Angels.

The next day, then, fortified by careful lesson planning and by earnest prayer, she tried once more to bring an atmosphere of Christianity into the classroom. In her pocket she carried a little bundle of tickets, which the other Sisters had helped her to prepare the evening before. In her heart she carried a great deal of courage and zeal, together with at least a little trepidation.

To her amazement, all was quiet. The little rogues of yesterday seemed to be subdued. Had a miracle occurred? Her confidence rising, Sister Theodore stepped forward briskly and began to speak. How attentively they listened! Too late it dawned on her that they were *too* attentive. Not even grace normally worked that fast. What was coming next?

She was not long in finding out. At a sign from the leader, they all jumped up and began a lively dance. Faster and faster they spun around, to the tune of a carefree song which grew louder and louder. Flushed of face and getting breathless, the miscreants stole sly glances to see how Sister was taking it. To their astonishment, she wasn't getting excited. She wasn't weeping. She wasn't ranting at them. She just stood, waiting. She even looked pleased, as though she enjoyed watching little ones amuse themselves.

Even the rowdiest children get tired of frisking sooner or later. In this case, they tired of dancing before Sister tired of watching; they had perforce to stop, and they were glad to drop into their seats. Then Sister Theodore moved, and while all eyes followed her, she reached for the switch. Hypnotized, they watched her, their heads still spinning a little too much to think of action. What was she going to do? Somebody gasped. Slowly, calmly, deliberately, Sister was breaking the switch, breaking it into little tiny pieces which she dropped into the coal basket. Then she turned to them.

"Now, children," she said, "as I was telling you a little while ago, God loves you very much. He wants to see you happy. I, too, wish to make you happy. While you are resting, let me tell you of my plans." She drew the little pack of tickets from her capacious pocket. "We shall commence today. The little girls who have their lessons well done and receive no demerits for conduct will each receive a ticket. You must save your tickets, for with them you can earn many prizes and frolics. Now let us commence the work for today." Baffled, they raised their weary little heads to listen to her. Her successful campaign had begun.


## Decorations

7 The effects of the victory won that day in the classroom spread through the school and out to the families of the poor, underprivileged little girls with whom the Sisters worked. Bit by bit Sister Theodore and her school gained the respect and gratitude of the people of Rennes, from the bishop down to the humblest pupil. As discipline

improved, so did instruction. Eventually the industrial school in which Sister Theodore began her work became one of the largest and most flourishing in France; yet in speaking of it, those who knew Sister Theodore called it with reason "her school."

Sister Theodore remained at Rennes for ten hardworking and successful years. She was reverenced on every side, but what she prized most was the appreciation and regard of her superior, Mother Mary. "I come to Sister Theodore's house to rest," the superior would remark. "I know that everything here is in perfect order." Mother Mary entrusted to Sister Theodore the founding of other schools in Rennes, some for the poor and underprivileged, some for the wealthier classes; and with all of them Sister was successful. She was not afraid to beg for assistance for the children in her schools, and she prevailed on many good people to share their riches with the poor and the orphans. Honored and trusted by all, and confident that she was serving God and His people, she was very happy at Rennes.

She was quite unprepared, then, for the summons she received one day towards the end of the school year, to leave Rennes and repair to a little country place called Soulaines. In all those first trying days with unruly children, shiftless and resentful parents, discouragement of every kind, her courage had not failed her. Now she found that courage of a different kind was needed. Naturally it was hard to leave a place where one was loved and respected, to say good-bye to those who had become dear friends; but for all this, as a good religious, Sister Theodore was always ready. Hardest of all was to feel that somehow she had unwittingly lost the confidence of her superiors.

It was the Bishop of Rennes himself who helped her bear this harsh trial. "I regret very sincerely," he wrote her, "that circumstances have not permitted you to return to your establishment, which will never forget the good you have done in it." And again, when she was settled at Soulaines, "In the midst of the sick and the dying you are called upon to take care of both body and soul. Why, it is almost an apostolate you exercise. I am prompted to say that God treats you almost as a spoiled child, and that, more than ever, He shows that He has designs upon you of great mercy."

As Bishop de Lesquin foresaw, the change of duties was for Sister Theodore a providential event. The quiet life at Soulaines afforded her opportunities for the prayer and reading that she loved; the new type of work widened the scope of her talents. In order the better to care for the sick, she took a regular course in medicine, gaining skill which was to be of great advantage to her later. Dr. Lecacheur, her instructor, gave her valuable help in diagnosing and treating illness, and in preparing medicines.

Much of her time was spent in visiting the sick and the poor, of whom there were many in the parish. Soon she became a familiar figure. Little ones would watch for her from doorsteps as she made her way down the rutted roads. "Here comes Sister Theodore! Now we shall have warm clothes! I saw her first! I get to carry her basket!"

"No, you carried it last time. It is my turn. Mother is feeling better, Sister Theodore! Your medicine helped her."

"I am glad of that, my dear. Come now, you must help, too. Let me show you how to prepare this nourishing gruel for your mother. And you, Céline, you must fix this milk for the little ones." It was a happy day in the poor little hovels when Sister Theodore made her visit.

Sometimes a sick old man would look up at her with rheumy eyes and stammer, "I didn't think you could get here today, Sister, with the roads so muddy, and all the rain."

"It would take more than a little rain and mud to keep me from my friends," she would say, watching the moisture from her heavy skirt splash on the dusty floor. "Now see what good Madame Butal has made for you. This soup is just what you need, and then you shall have some preserves."

With increasing satisfaction, Father Brillouet, the curé, watched her activities among his parishioners. Then one day he approached her with a request of his own.

"I cannot thank you enough, Sister, for what you are doing for my people. There have been more at Mass and the sacraments these past few months. Finding that there is someone to care, having decent clothing, enough food, is a big help to devotion."

"Your own efforts are untiring, Father." Sister Theodore was not merely trying to return a compliment; she found the pastor's zeal an inspiration, and his encouragement an incentive.

"Sometimes, though," he said whimsically, "my efforts are not enough. Just now, for instance, Sister, I come to ask you to supplement them."

"But how, Father?"

"You know how much my parishioners and I long to build a suitable church to replace our old and dilapidated one."

"Yes, Father, many of them have spoken of it to me, deploring their lack of means."

"Ah, yes, they have good will. But the means . . ."

"But I thought Monsieur was going to help." "Monsieur" was the one wealthy person in the neighborhood, Monsieur Perrault de la Bertaudière. An aristocrat, he had lost much of his fortune in the Revolution; but the remnant saved for him by a faithful servant left him still a very rich man, and his generosity matched his riches. With his help, Sister Theodore pondered, what could hinder the erection of a beautiful church?

But there were complications. Persuaded that people would think he was trying to set himself up as a philanthropist, Monsieur had withdrawn his offer of help. "I don't know whose imprudent remarks influenced him," sighed Father Brillouet, "but he has suddenly and effectively changed his mind."

"Is that possible? With all his good will?"

"It has happened, Sister. All seemed so smooth at the first; we were so confident, so happy. And now no one can move him. He will listen to no arguments."

Sister Theodore was genuinely distressed. But what could she do? "I will ask the other Sisters to pray for a change of heart, Father."

"You must do more, Sister. God helps those who help themselves, you know. By all means pray, but please lend us your efforts, too. Sister, you must see Monsieur for us and beg him to reconsider."

In vain Sister Theodore pleaded that she could not succeed where the curé and the best of the parishioners had failed. "He has such regard for you, Sister Theodore. If you cannot prevail upon him, no one can, and we must give up our dream. But I have full confidence in you. Sister, I know you will succeed."

Finally, she did succeed. She had to use all her persuasive powers, and bolster all her efforts with fervent prayer, but Monsieur gave in. He would go on with the building of the church. He himself would finance it completely. It would be a thing of beauty, a place worthy of the worship of God and the uplift of souls. The happy curé and a committee of the parishioners began immediately to discuss plans with Monsieur de la Bertaudière. When the cornerstone was laid, Sister Theodore's name was placed in the manuscript cemented there.

Life at Soulaines brought work in the classroom, too, and this was work which Sister Theodore loved and in which she always excelled. An official visit from the school inspectors of Angers did not daunt her classes at all and so impressed the examiners that they praised her highly to the Board of Education. One day not long after this visit Sister Theodore was busy at one of her favorite tasks—helping in the kitchen.

Since the staff at Soulaines was very small indeed—besides Sister Theodore there were only two other Sisters—there was always plenty of work for all, and Sister Theodore enjoyed doing her share. Her habit protected by a voluminous apron, she was busily scouring the pans.

"If you will start the soup for supper early, Sister," she was saying to her companion, "we can get in a visit to poor Madame Pinard this afternoon, and . . ." Suddenly a knock sounded. "Ah, there is Jean with the vegetables at last." Sister Theodore wiped her hands and hurried to the door. It was only as she opened to two distinguished gentlemen that she remembered her apron. But she did not lose her poise.

"You will pardon me, Messieurs," she said, "I was not expecting guests!"

"But not at all, Madame!" It was they who seemed abashed, as with great deference they removed their hats and bowed to her. "We have the honor to visit you on behalf of the Academy, which has been pleased to vote you medallion decorations in token of your excellence in teaching."

"I am indeed honored, gentlemen," said the surprised Sister.

"On the contrary, Madame, the honor is ours. You are to be sincerely congratulated. Your establishment is a credit to our town. We count ourselves fortunate to have you among us."

As they bowed themselves out, the two visitors exchanging expressions of admiration, Sister Theodore blushingly confiding her testimonial to her capacious pocket, there came from the direction of the kitchen the sound of rapturous applause.

"We couldn't help but overhear a little," confessed Sister St. Edmond. "Do let us see it, Sister!"

Sister Theodore had to show her letter of commendation.

"Ah! These inspectors really do know their business, after all. You see even they recognize merit. You must write to Mother Mary about it, Sister."

"And you must show it to everyone! Think of the prestige for our school!"

Sister Theodore had no intention of exhibiting her award. She reckoned, however, without the school authorities. In the interest of education, they decided, it was only fitting that outstanding merit be publicly acknowledged; therefore they had to insist that Sister Theodore receive medallion honors in the presence of the curé and the town officials.

As he watched the proceedings with approval, Father Brillouet reflected that he had more than one reason to be grateful to Providence for sending Sister Theodore to Soulaines. His people were happier and more faithful to their duties; the children were being well instructed; and the dream of his heart, a beautiful church where all might unite to share the Mass and the sacraments, was about to be realized. It took shape in his mind: frescoed ceiling, gilded cornice, marble floor, the beautiful altar with its six stately pillars, the broad central aisle. He had reason to be grateful to Sister Theodore.

With all his heart he hoped that the rumor he had heard, that Sister Theodore was going to be taken from them, to be sent—of all places!—to *America,* was in fact only a rumor. Such an idea was unthinkable, frail as she was in health (as Dr. Lecacheur said, it would be like condemning her to death!). And then she was necessary here, and America was so far away!

## Who Will Go?

**8** During the years since Sister Theodore's entrance, Father Dujarié's foundation at Ruillé had prospered. Under Mother Mary's capable direction, the community, now numbering over two hundred, conducted schools in twelve dioceses of France. From all sides came requests for Sisters to open schools, to nurse the sick, and to take charge of orphanages. The request that came in the late summer of 1839, however, caused much excitement and surprise.

On August 20 of that year, Sister Portress opened the door to a man of tall, imposing figure who introduced himself as Monseigneur Célestin de la Hailandière, newly appointed Bishop of Vincennes, Indiana. "Your Reverend Superior has given me the honor of an appointment with her."

"Ah, yes, Monseigneur. Reverend Mother is expecting you." Sister ushered him into the parlor, where Mother Mary and Sister St. Charles promptly joined him.

"I have come hundreds of leagues, Reverend Mother," he began, "to beg for help for my poor diocese in America."

"We shall try to give you what alms we can, Your Excellency."

"Ah, yes, it's true we need material alms, but I am applying to others for those. The alms I ask of you, you alone can give; I beg you to give me some of your Sisters to open schools in my needy diocese. I have observed the work of your Sisters in Rennes; I am sure their help would be invaluable in Indiana."

"Give you Sisters, Monseigneur? But all our work is here in France. We had not thought of entering the foreign missions!"

"Then, Reverend Mother, I beg you to think of it now. If you only knew the need!" On fire with his subject, Bishop de la Hailandière proceeded to give Mother Mary a description of the vast diocese, stretching from the Ohio River to the Great Lakes, populated by souls of French, Irish, English, German backgrounds, only a sixth of whom called themselves Catholics; and these last were without schools, churches, even priests. It was true that there were thirty priests now, whereas in 1834 the entire diocese had had only one; still, what were thirty in such a field? These priests were truly missionaries, traveling like the Apostles from one place to another, living on alms, often going hungry and sleeping in the woods.

Mother Mary, familiar with conditions in her own country during and after the Revolution, was immediately sympathetic. "But how do you manage at all, Monseigneur?" she asked. "How do you keep up your churches? Who cares for your altars?"

His smile was rueful. "Churches, Mother? In our diocese we have no churches as you understand them. In Vincennes, it is true, there is a brick cathedral; but you must not compare it with your Notre Dame. But Vincennes is the seat of the diocese. Most of our churches elsewhere are mere cabins made of logs hewn from our great forests, thatched with moss, bare of furniture. As for our altars and linens, the priest carries with him the vestments and vessels needed for Mass and the sacraments, and often they are as worn and threadbare as his own attire.

"Sometimes weeks go by during which the people have no sight of a priest. Do you wonder, then, Reverend Mother, that in a country like America, in a region of that country like the opening Midwest, where the people are filled with independence, initiative, and ambition, they should almost forget that they have souls? You cannot realize the indifference, the unbelief we find on the part of Catholics—the bigotry and open attacks that come from some outside the Church. My predecessor, Bishop Bruté, the first Bishop of Vincennes, labored beyond his strength to remedy these evils; now that I have been consecrated bishop, I hope to do all I can; but I must have help."

"Whatever help we might give, Monseigneur, would be so little in such a plight!"

"But even a little would help, Reverend Mother. Already the Brothers of Holy Cross, of Le Mans, have promised their help towards a school for the boys. If you can only give us some Sisters to teach the girls and to nurse the sick, how much that will mean!"

Impressed as Mother Mary was by Bishop de la Hailandière's appeal, and eager as she was to help, she realized that there were many facets of the problem to consider. "Let us think about it and discuss it among ourselves, Your Excellency. Our community will gather next month for retreat. Then you shall have our answer."

It was not a definite "Yes," but somehow Monseigneur de la Hailandière took his leave confident that the Sisters of Providence would come to his aid. And, indeed, the Chapter agreed that such a plea as his should not go unheeded. The decision was approved by the Bishop of Le Mans, Monseigneur Bouvier. Being both prudent and practical, however, Mother Mary decided that before committing the community in any way, she should be sure that there was someone among its members who could carry the burden of the new venture. As she called to mind the qualifications of all her daughters, she saw no one so well fitted as Sister Theodore. I shall not tell her that she must go, however, Mother Mary reflected. No Sister will be asked to go. It must all be voluntary.

That August the magic names of "Vincennes," "America," "Indiana," "the missions," were familiar words around Ruillé. There were many volunteers. Who would be permitted to go? To some of the Sisters, it seemed a great privilege, to others a costly adventure to be dared for Christ. To some it represented a sacrifice which would prove their love for God, or a chance to make Him better known in the world. As for Sister Theodore, it was a matter of earnest prayer that the superiors might be guided in their choice of missionaries. She herself, she felt, was completely unfit. Her feeble health alone would prevent her from having the temerity to volunteer. She and her two companions from Soulaines arrived at Ruillé eager to learn details of the project.

"Reverend Mother has told Monseigneur that she

has only one Sister capable of leading such a mission," one of the Sisters at the mother house told them. Sister Theodore, never dreaming that she was that one Sister, prayed that the mission might not fail for lack of leadership.

It was not long, however, before she learned that unless she gave that leadership, the project would not be undertaken at all. At last, seeing all her protestations of unworthiness set aside and all the opportunities for courageous sacrifice laid before her, she agreed to direct the new mission.

From the list of volunteers, the superiors chose three other Sisters and two novices to accompany Sister Theodore. The chosen ones were Sister St. Vincent Ferrer, Sister Basilide, Sister Olympiade, Sister St. Liguori, and Sister Mary Xavier. Bishop de la Hailandière had recruited also a gifted and zealous young woman from Saint-Servan, Irma Le Fer de la Motte, who was admitted at Ruillé at his special request to prepare herself for the American mission. They would have a year to prepare, and leave for Indiana in the summer of 1840.

That year was one of excited activity. Across the Atlantic, Bishop de la Hailandière, delighted to have the Sisters for his diocese, set about planning a dwelling for them. The Sisters selected returned to their missions in France, filled with thoughts of the future. Sister Theodore expressed their sentiments in a letter to Irma Le Fer de la Motte. "It is a great honor to be chosen for the grand work of enkindling the light of faith in a country where His adorable name is scarcely heard. . . . Many there who claim to be Catholics do not know how to make the sign of the Cross, it is said; much less do they know the Our Father and the Hail Mary; and some do not even know that God created them."

Sister Theodore was evidently convinced that it was a wild and pagan country to which she was going. She was prepared for the very worst; and Mother

Mary was careful not to minimize the difficulties of the venture lest her Sisters proceed under any illusions. None should feel that it was a matter of obedience; for all it should be an opportunity for loving sacrifice.

As time went on, Sister Theodore found herself growing more and more eager for her new mission. She realized, of course, that many of the sacrifices would be on the part of those the Sisters were leaving behind them in France, among them her own sister Marie-Jeanne, who now as Madame LeTouzé was still living at Étables. To her she wrote, "Do not be grieved, my dear Marie, if I say that I can no longer feel satisfied at home. I must get at the work awaiting me at Vincennes. I long for the time to come, and yet my heart will all but break, for I love you all, my dear Ruillé, my beloved France; yes, I love you all, but I must go; it is God's will. Pray always for me and for those who are to share my grand destiny."

The date set for their departure for the seaport was July 16, 1840, feast of Our Lady of Mount Carmel. At four o'clock that morning the little band of missionaries and their friends gathered for the last time in the cathedral of Le Mans. Bishop Bouvier's secretary, Canon Lottin, was there to offer Mass and impart his farewell blessing. His final gift to them was a relic of the true Cross.

"You have given yourselves to a great work," he told them, "but you will have to suffer much. With the Cross and through the Cross and in the Cross you will conquer."

And so, encouraged and inspired, they set out for Le Havre.

# *America!*

**9** From the bustling deck of the sailing vessel *Cincinnati*, the missionaries took their last long look at France. How quickly its shores seemed to disappear! Ahead of them now lay forty days between sea and sky, among strangers speaking an unfamiliar tongue.

They were eventful days. Even as Sister Theodore turned from the fading coast line to her companions, all bravely trying to hide their heartache, there was a disturbance at her side. She saw two dark forms hurtle over the rail; while the astonished passengers looked down, a mocking cry of "Adieu!" floated back from a rowboat making for shore at top speed, and carrying, with two of the crew, a sizeable amount of the passengers' money. The Sisters were among those despoiled.

"God is truly asking us to trust His Providence," said Sister Theodore. "More than ever we must put all our confidence in Him. Although we had little enough money to start with, having lost part of it we are more in His hands."

"Yes," agreed Sister Basilide. "Didn't Christ tell the Apostles to go without scrip or purse? And we still have something! May God reward the Countess de Marescot for her generous gift!" Hidden in a box marked "Confections" sent by the countess as a farewell present, they had found a sorely needed supply of gold pieces, which fortunately had not been with the stolen money.

On several nights they heard shouts of "Thieves!" and much commotion in the hold. After dinner one day three unkempt, half-starved, quaking men were dragged before the captain. They were indeed robbers who had escaped from prison and stowed themselves on the ship. The kindly captain, after blustering a bit, ordered food to be brought to the starving wretches, and set them to work until he could transfer them to a ship returning to Havre.

There was no chaplain on board. As darkness settled, the Sisters went below to recite their Office and rosary; often other passengers joined them, and this took the place of all religious services on board. Among the passengers was a Breton, Thomas Brassier, with his wife and six children. He was hoping to build a home in the New World, and before the voyage ended he had agreed to settle in Indiana and work for the new community.

Early on the morning of Friday, September 4, they caught sight at last of land. Trembling with excitement, the Sisters hurried up the narrow little stairs to the deck, expecting to look upon a scene of untamed natural beauty. What they saw was breathtaking— stretches of patterned landscape, beautiful mansions sparkling in the early morning sun. Where were the dense thickets, the Indian wigwams?

"Could anything be more beautiful?" cried Sister Theodore. "At every turn we find compensation for our sacrifices." They noted the beautifully kept gardens, the stately entrance to New York harbor, "according to general opinion the most beautiful sight it is possible to behold!"

There was no one to meet them at the harbor, however. As the faces of American travelers lighted with recognition of their friends; as other strangers to America were warmly greeted and welcomed, the Sisters looked in vain for someone to take them in charge. It was the quarantine officer, Dr. Sydney Doane, who graciously put them at ease. "It is a blessing to have you in America," he told them in their own tongue. "Soon you will be surrounded by numerous friends who will be happy to see you. The bishop will be much pleased to know of your arrival; I shall carry your messages to him myself, if you wish."

It was a good thing Dr. Doane spoke French. The gratitude of the Sisters could not have been expressed in any other language. Dr. Doane made them still more his debtors when he returned a short time later, bearing a basket of fruit and other refreshments. "This fruit is from my own garden; I can guarantee it," he said with a laugh.

He was there, too, when they landed the next afternoon, to take them first to his own home and then to that of a distinguished and charitable New York lady, Mrs. André Parmentier, widow of the noted Belgian horticulturist who had founded the first Botanical Gardens at New York. Mrs. Parmentier's beautiful Brooklyn home was always open to missionaries arriving for work in the great mission field that was America in the early nineteenth century. She received the Sisters, as Sister Theodore expressed it, "like angels from heaven," and enlisted for them also the services of a friend of hers, Mr. Samuel Byerley.

It was well that America was so friendly to them, for their situation on arrival was precarious and embarrassing. From the Bishop of Vincennes there had come no message, no representative, no funds. They decided to seek out his agent in Philadelphia.

Along the way the Sisters marveled at the wonders of the New World. The beauty of many churches, the piety of the people in what they had considered an unevangelized land, amazed them.

"There are as many men as women at Mass," they exclaimed.

"And there is not one woman without a bonnet!"

Other things about America astonished them, too. "What a stylish conveyance!" exclaimed Sister Olympiade, noticing a trim white wagon rattling over the cobbles, drawn by two horses. To an American, it was just the milkman; to Sister Olympiade it looked like the President's carriage.

"And that young man," added Sister Theodore,

indicating the whistling milkman in his crisp white suit, "might be dressed for a wedding!"

"How extravagant these Americans are!" said Sister Basilide.

"But how hospitable, how courteous, how kind!"

The kindness of New York was duplicated in Philadelphia, where Bishop Conwell received them graciously and commended them to the care of the Sisters of Charity. Sister Theodore was charmed with Philadelphia. "Except the public monuments, I do not think I have seen anything in Paris that approaches the richness and splendor of this 'Queen City of America.'"

While they were in Philadelphia, a French-Canadian priest arrived on his way to Vincennes. "You would do well to travel west with him," advised Bishop Conwell. Sister Theodore agreed. Their journey led them from Philadelphia to Baltimore to Cincinnati; everywhere they received hospitality from the Sisters of Charity. They shared the prayers, the simple meals, and, even though they could not freely converse with one another, the pleasant recreations of these American religious, who were so filled with the spirit of humility and poverty that Sister Theodore loved.

As they traveled westward they discovered a different America from that of the magnificent, opulent seaboard, a "new world within the New World." Instead of the broad avenues of the East, there were steep and dangerous roads, treacherous streams; instead of beautiful homes, rude log cabins surrounded by patches of land where trees had been burned to provide room for raising corn and grazing the animals which were the only capital of the frontier Americans. It was a relief to disembark at Cincinnati after a painful four-day voyage on a wretched riverboat where thirty passengers occupied accommodations for twelve.

As they stepped on the wharf, a small, slight man advanced to meet them. "I am Bishop Purcell," he

[ 49 ]

told them. "You are welcome indeed in my diocese."

To their great surprise, the bishop himself began at once to help unload their trunks and to carry their bags. "You are now on the confines of your mission," he said, "for the Bishop of Vincennes and I are vicars for each other. But you are not even to think of going farther until you have rested. I have carriages here to take you to the Sisters of Charity." Gratefully the Sisters followed him. For the first time in seven days they could go properly to rest.

They awoke to realize that they were now indeed in missionary country. They wept at the poverty and destitution of the cathedral at Cincinnati; at Louisville they talked with Father Badin, the first priest ordained in the United States, who had many stories to tell of his fifty years of labor on the frontier. They admired the Sisters of Charity, who shared with them their boiled potatoes and corn bread; and the American Catholics, whom they found to have "the spirit of the Christians of the primitive Church: great charity, the love of hospitality which St. Paul recommends so strongly, an ardent zeal for the cause of the Gospel, in fine, all the virtues of the Fathers of the Faith."

Finally, at a little inn at Madison, Indiana, they were joined by their own bishop. So startled were they by his appearance that they could scarcely return his greeting. He wore secular clothing, old and frayed; his boots were caked with dried mud which left little flakes on the carpet as he moved about. His face was weather-beaten, brown, windburned. Was this the stately and regal bishop they had met in France?

"No doubt you wondered why your bishop had not sent for you," he said. "You will soon learn, Sisters, that it is not always possible for me to do as I would wish. I had not a single priest, not one, whom I could send, for all are either ill or far too busy. But the Lord has taken care of you. What a relief to see you at last!"

"We are eager to be at our destination, Your Excellency, and to begin our work."

"You will find a place awaiting you," he told them, "not quite completed, but well on the way. You have not far to go now; it is near Terre Haute. But I shall see you again in Vincennes within two weeks. There we shall discuss our affairs."

At Vincennes they found a cathedral which surpassed in poverty that of Cincinnati, "a brick building with large windows without curtains; most of the panes of glass broken . . . a poor wooden altar, a railing unfinished and yet seemingly decaying with age. The bishop's seat is an old red chair which even our peasants would not have in what they consider a nice room." The bishop's house, too, was small and ramshackle, with broken steps and flaked paint. All that it contained was open to the priests of the diocese.

Their own house was to be located some sixty miles from Vincennes. With Father Buteux, their newly appointed chaplain, to direct them, the Sisters left the little town of Vincennes at ten o'clock at night on October 20, on the last lap of their long journey.

## Golden October

**10** Father Buteux signaled the driver; the carriage stopped. "Come down, Sisters," cried the priest. "We have arrived!"

Emerging from the coach, the Sisters looked around. To their astonishment, they found themselves still in the midst of a forest, without a village or even a house in sight. The late afternoon sun scarcely penetrated the density of the foliage. The stillness all around was broken only by a gentle rustle here and there in the treetops, or the scurry of a little wood creature among the fallen leaves. Here was a wilderness indeed!

As the Sisters stood in amazement, Father Buteux pointed across a ravine to where the outline of a frame house was just visible through the trees. "There you will lodge until your own house is ready. But first we will go to the church."

The Sisters had agreed among themselves that they would speak to no one until they had first visited the Blessed Sacrament. The "church" to which Father led them was a little log cabin thirteen by fifteen feet, typical of the rude mission chapels of those times. There was no tabernacle, but only a small silver pyx contained in a little case called a "custode," made of pasteboard and cloth and tied with a drawstring. There was no altar, but only a table made from three planks resting on stakes driven into the bare ground. The strictly necessary vessels stood on a little table, covered with a piece of dark blue calico. A poor old bed, a couple of small tables and rickety chairs completed the furnishings of this combination church, rectory, and convent chapel.

Kneeling in silence, the missionaries renewed the offering of their lives in God's service. It was this poverty and humility, after all, that they had come to share. They had an excellent example, too, in their chaplain, of whom Sister Theodore later wrote, "Here it is that for four years this Parisian has dwelt, he who was brought up in one of the most luxurious cities in Europe, and who now in the flower of his age, with his brilliant education, might be prominent in ecclesiastical circles and occupy an important position. The Archbishop of Paris made him the most advantageous offers to retain him, but he refused everything to come and suffer for his God and to gain souls for Him. He boards with the farmer who lodges us."

This farmer was Joseph Thralls, owner of the farmhouse in which for six weeks four postulants had been awaiting the arrival of the French Sisters. Since early morning on this eventful day the four young women had been taking turns scanning the path through the forest. Everything in the house was just as ready as they could make it. They had helped Mrs. Thralls set the table, gather firewood, and fry the chicken for a special gala dinner. That dinner had been pushed from back to front of the stove time and again when the travelers continued to be delayed. Now at last they were here. With joy and awe the Americans ran out to meet them and help remove their wet and muddy cloaks.

"We thought you would never come," timidly ventured Mary Doyle. She was encouraged when Sister Theodore smilingly replied, "And we thought we should never arrive!"

Mr. Thralls had a huge fire kindled; in the light of its homey blaze all sat down to the waiting dinner. While the American girls hovered about the Sisters, motherly Mrs. Thralls whisked the oft-heated chicken to the table, and in broken French and broken English the little groups met and mingled.

Since the Sisters' house was not yet ready, the generous farmer and his family of ten offered to share the sturdy farmhouse equally with them, giving them one of the two rooms and one half of the cornloft. The one room was to serve the Sisters as workroom, refectory, recreation room, and infirmary combined. In one section of the loft were lined up eight little straw ticks on the floor under a loosely shingled roof. For kitchen, there was a stove in an open shed.

The missionaries had to wait until morning before penetrating the forest to view their own unfinished house. They found it hidden like a little castle among the oaks and beeches, the elms and maples—a small two-story brick building, severely simple. It could not possibly be ready before spring.

There in the midst of the woods, in the bright October sunshine, the Sisters looked at one another and took stock of their resources. With five pairs of eager French eyes turned towards her, to say nothing of the wondering, hopeful glances of the young Ameri-

[ 53 ]

cans, Sister Theodore smiled. "We can make a real convent of our share of the Thralls house for now," she said. "Already all the strict necessities are there. We have a place to pray, to eat, and—to sleep." They all nodded agreement. Nobody mentioned what might happen in the loft in case of rain or snow.

"If we live our Rule from the very beginning," continued Sister Theodore, "we shall surely have God's blessing on our mission. When we return to the house we shall sit down and plan what can be done."

"We truly have a beautiful garden, Sister," declared Sister St. Liguori, as they walked back through the fallen leaves. "Just look at all this great woods in such a riot of color!"

"There are berries, too, lots of them. We can show you," cried Joséphine. "We have found many good patches."

"Our postulants have not been idle, I see." Sister Olympiade was already planning menus. "You shall show us where to find the best."

"There are wild grapes, too, across the ravine!"

"And lots of nuts — and apples!"

"You can all help me gather them, but I think first you will have to help me learn a little of your English," said Sister Olympiade with a laugh.

No sooner had they regained the house than the organization began. Mrs. Thralls readily offered the use of the dining room table. With this as headquarters, Sister Theodore detailed responsibilities. Sister St. Vincent would be sacristan; Sister Olympiade, of course, would be cook. Sister St. Liguori would help acquaint the postulants with their duties, and they in turn would keep the large room neat and orderly, learn how to serve at table and wash the dishes. Sister Basilide was still suffering from the fever she had caught on the way, and Sister Mary Xavier had now fallen prey to it; their main duty for the present would be to get well. Sister Theodore would supervise and plan, secure supplies and equipment, and begin to

young ladies eager to come. It will be hard for them at first, perhaps, with their independent spirit, but you will find them possessed of very fine characters, and eager to learn."

This, indeed, was the case. Despite the difference in temperament and the effort it cost to overcome their natural pride, the young Americans delighted the Sisters by their wholehearted earnestness and generosity.

One thing Monseigneur had objected to. Hearing the others speak of Sister Theodore as "the superior," he shook his head. "You must call her 'Mother,' " he commanded. In some ways this was an easy command to obey, for the Sisters were happy to give this title of respect to one whose leadership had not failed them; on the other hand, it cost the French Sisters a little pang to pronounce so far from their mother house this name filled with memories of Ruillé.

Mother Theodore's first concern was to prepare teachers for the academy which they would open as soon as the building was ready and pupils could be found. An excellent teacher herself, she was hopeful that the new schools founded under her supervision would offer young Americans the very best in instruction. Education in pioneer days was often haphazard. Teachers and pupils worked on the farms in late spring and summer, and gathered in primitive one-room schools in the fall. There were no well-equipped school libraries, colorful maps and charts, and only homemade "audio-visual aids." In some cases, even real textbooks were wanting.

In many American cities, however, private academies offered a broad curriculum, always including music. As they passed through some of these cities in their travel westward, the Sisters had not failed to learn all they could of American educational ideals and methods. They spent the long winter days studying English and preparing classwork according to American standards and their own excellent traditions.

[ 57 ]

In July, 1841, the first academy at St. Mary's opened, ready to teach "English composition and rhetoric, natural philosophy, chemistry, botany, mythology, biography, French, German, needlework, bead and lace work,"—but still awaiting beds and other material conveniences. The first pupil, Mary Lenoble, arrived on July 4; the next day came Sarah Williams from Terre Haute and Susan and Elizabeth Lalumiere from Vincennes. Finally, thirteen girls assembled on July 7, 1841, for the first Mass of the Holy Spirit and the opening session of St. Mary's Institute.

It was a small beginning, but eventually the enrollment began to increase steadily. The Sisters were kept busy cording wool and filling straw mattresses, each one striving to be the first to sacrifice her own when a newcomer arrived unexpectedly. Mother Theodore shared in every phase of the labor, encouraging the pupils by her personal concern for them, and the Sisters by her interest in their work and her daily instructions, in which she tried to impress on them the beauty of their lives as teachers.

"Have you ever thought, dear Sisters," she would remind them, "that you are privileged to do on earth what Our Lord did? He instructed and you instruct. He was often surrounded by little children, and you spend your lives among them; it is truly sublime to be devoted to the service of our neighbor. But we must not think it an easy task. We must possess all the virtues before we attempt to teach them to others.

"Let us be generous and self-sacrificing," she encouraged, when there was hard work to do and not even enough bread to eat. "Let us trust in Providence, on whom we rely for all!" They had the joy of seeing their trust rewarded as young women entered the novitiate and satisfied parents recommended the academy to their friends. Before the end of their first year in the forest, the little academy was well established, roads and walks had been constructed through the woods, and the gardens were producing. There were ten girls in training in the novitiate, and the original farmhouse was being enlarged.

Then, in mid-November, came a long-awaited joy. Sister St. Francis Xavier (Irma Le Fer de la Motte), her year of waiting in France finally over, arrived at St. Mary's after a long and eventful voyage. With five Sacred Heart nuns, she had joined at Le Havre a group of missionaries headed by Father Sorin, who was accompanied by six Brothers from Le Mans. Exceedingly frail and delicate, Sister St. Francis had suffered intensely during the crossing. At New York, after experiencing like the Sisters before her the kindness of the Parmentiers and Mr. Byerley, she had joined a group bound for Vincennes. It was seven o'clock on the evening of November 15 when at last Mother Theodore had the happiness of welcoming this earnest young religious, who was to be a consolation to her compatriots and an inspiration to the young Americans.

A few days later there arrived at St. Mary's another young woman who was to prove of great assistance to the new community. This was Miss Eleanor Bailly, daughter of a Canadian fur trader, a talented, highly educated girl, destined to succeed Mother Theodore as superior. She was the first postulant entrusted to Sister St. Francis, who shortly after her arrival was assigned the care of the novitiate.

It was not long before requests came for Sisters to establish schools in other parts of the diocese. Wisely, Mother Theodore hesitated to send Sisters out to found establishments before they had themselves become well-grounded both spiritually and intellectually. The first foundation outside the forest at St. Mary-of-the-Woods was made at Jasper in 1842, in response to the pleas of the Reverend Joseph Kundek.

It was an amazing journey that Mother Theodore and the three Sisters she was taking to Jasper made that spring, setting out from St. Mary's by wagon on March 14, crossing the Wabash in an Indian canoe, and wading to the shore in mud to their knees; thence by steamboat to Vincennes, and from there to Washington, Indiana, by stage. From Washington the next day a small cavalcade set out—the bishop on horseback, followed by Mother Theodore, Sister St. Vincent, and a little girl in a carriage, and then Sister Marie Joseph and Sister Gabriella in a wagon. Neither the German driver of the carriage nor his passengers had a great command of English, or, as a matter of fact, of the terrain. Before long they were lost in the thick woods, where they were finally rescued by some workmen. Tired, hungry, and bewildered, they at last reached Jasper, where the bishop, worried at their delay, was praying earnestly for their safety.

The mission at Jasper was opened on the feast of St. Joseph, March 19, 1842, with a beautiful ceremony in which most of the town took part. Father Kundek loved to arrange colorful pageants, and on this beautiful spring day a procession of the Blessed Sacrament, led by the bishop, wound through streets decorated with banners and garlands, lined with pupils and parishioners eager to welcome the new teachers.

Unfortunately, this welcome was soon clouded by the atmosphere of intolerance that pervaded the settlement. For this reason, as well as for the poverty of the school and the loneliness of the Sisters separated from St. Mary's and often left without the sacraments while the pastor was away on missionary journeys, Jasper was long the subject of Mother Theodore's prayers and concern. She did what she could for the little mission, St. Mary's "eldest daughter."

Later in the same year the second foundation was made, this time at St. Francisville, a little French-Canadian village near Vincennes, reached by the old Indian trail which George Rogers Clark had tramped in Revolutionary days. Here, as at Jasper, the duties of the Sisters included, besides teaching classes, caring for the church, cooking and mending for the pastor, cultivating their own garden, and milking their cow.

The pastor at St. Francisville was particularly proud of their "incomparable cow," from which the Sisters obtained butter, cream for coffee, and "fresh sweet milk which is an excellent drink."

Not every feature of the St. Francisville mission, however, was worthy of such praise. There, as at Jasper, the Sisters met prejudice and poverty; there the young superior, Sister St. Liguori, contracted the disease which helped to shorten her life.

Meanwhile the Sisters had begun to teach the children of the village at St. Mary-of-the-Woods. In this apostolate Sister St. Francis excelled. Writing to her family, she described the "big boys of fifteen who have not yet made their First Communion," and children born of Catholic parents "who have never heard of God."

"Shall I speak to you of our little boys," she writes, "as poor and ignorant as my boldest ambitions could desire? I had the happiness of teaching one that he has a soul and that there is a God. . . . The first time I explained the chapter on creation in the Bible to them I asked the difference between man and the other animals, but not one was able to answer; finally the wisest, after having attentively looked at the engraving in the Bible, blurted out: 'Sister, the difference is that a horse has four feet and a man only two!'"

One of the happiest recollections of the early Sisters was the beautiful ceremony of Christmas morning, 1843, when fifteen poor village children, the girls wearing veils used by the Sisters for the ceremony of taking the habit, some of the boys eighteen or nineteen years old, made their First Communion in the village church, which as yet had neither door nor window, and only an unfinished floor.

The cares attendant on the new establishment were not, however, the most harrowing of Mother Theodore's problems during the disastrous year of 1842. Early in that year she had the unhappy experience of finding that one of the young American novices of whom she had hoped much, and who had been greatly favored by the bishop in view of her future usefulness to the community, was in fact completely unfitted for the religious life. Further, this young woman, when regretfully dismissed, secured the help of friends in Terre Haute to open a school in competition with the struggling Institute at St. Mary-of-the-Woods. Thus not only was she herself a loss as a teacher, but her defection cost the Sisters pupils as well, just at a time when these were needed.

Because of the hard times everywhere, the Sisters had reduced the charges for the few pupils remaining to them. That was a year of strictest economy; often the merest necessities were wanting. Yet Mother Theodore saw in the destitution of the community only a further claim on Providence. "I believe Our Lord loves and protects these dear children, who for His love live here in the midst of the thick forest," she wrote to Ruillé. "His care of us shows His Providence." And she gave an instance. "The other day I did not know which way to turn. I did not have a penny, and I had to feed our household. Just then came a letter from Mr. Byerley with a hundred dollars."

It was well that her heart was filled with confidence, for new crosses were being prepared which would demand of her the utmost of courage and of trust.

## Flames in the Night

**12** "Thank you, Sister! It was so much fun!"

The five girls left at St. Mary-of-the-Woods during vacation let Sister Basilide go only as the vesper bell began to ring. She really was fun to be with, and the stories she could tell of her novitiate days in France! She had even known the founder of the Congregation, Father Dujarié.

"Well, sit down now and rest for a while," advised Sister. "You'll need some more energy if you want to help Sister Olympiade in her garden later on." A visit to Sister Olympiade's pharmacy and herb garden was one of the standard holiday attractions. Sister Basilide started with a quick, light step towards the chapel. The girls hurried up the academy steps.

"Come on, Sally, let's get your guitar! Coming, Mary Ann?"

Mary Ann Brown shook back her wind-tossed hair. "First I've a letter to write," she decided, looking thoughtfully after Sister Basilide. "I just don't see how Mary can keep up those foolish ideas of hers. If I could just persuade her to come here for a term, she'd see how mistaken she is!"

"Try again, anyway, but I don't suppose it will do any good. You know the wild tales people tell about convents — and Mary believes them!"

"Yes, like wearing pebbles in your shoes, and being locked up in the dark." Susan shivered. "I was uneasy myself when I first came."

"O Susan!" Mary Ann took out her little stationery case. "I'll start with the exciting things. She thinks we live like prisoners of war."

"Tell her about the music master," said Sally. "I think he was so romantic!"

"I don't think it was very romantic, dying of pleurisy. And I don't think there was any love tale connected with him after all. And we won't get a nobleman, either, for now his widow is going to take his classes!"

"Oh, you have such a drab outlook! Well, tell her about your prize for good behavior."

Mary Ann dipped her pen into the little glass inkwell. "It was a beautiful ivory tub with a purple velvet pincushion in it, and it came from France," she wrote.

Then there was the vacation to tell about, and the fun they had collecting maple sap and helping to make syrup. There was the bit of gossip about the music master and their disillusionment. Then, "If instead of visiting, you could persuade your mother and father to let you come to Saint Mary's, I should be so delighted! It would be of so much benefit to your health. You would have so much exercise, and this is the healthiest place in the state." The writer sighed and frowned at her pen. "Mary, I think there is no use persuading you to come, for fear of the dungeons you think we have. I have never seen them yet, and I suppose I never will."

The fears of Mary Ann's little friend were widespread in the 1840's when misguided lecturers and writers were dispensing such mistaken notions of the Church, of Catholic schools, and of convents in particular, that in some cases property was actually damaged. To religious intolerance was added a rising spirit of nativism which led to rioting and noisy demonstrations. It was Bishop Purcell's special invocation of Mary Immaculate against this tide of bigotry that led eventually to the naming of Mary as patroness of the United States under her title of the Immaculate Conception.

But that was to come later. In 1842 the Sisters at St. Mary's were among those who felt the effects of intolerance. The situation was particularly painful in Terre Haute, the town nearest to St. Mary's. When school opened in the fall, only one pupil from there returned, and she was a child who had nowhere else to go.

The failure of the boarding school would leave the Sisters with a mounting pile of debts and no way to pay them. To the French, the very necessity of contracting debts was a bitter cross. Fitted by their early training for living within their income, they found it hard to understand the ease with which Americans could buy on credit and pay in installments. Now, it

[ 64 ]

seemed, their creditors were unwilling to extend to them the privilege even of paying in installments. Whatever may have been the cause of the disaffection —wildly distorted ideas of convent life, distrust of foreigners, or false reports about the community in the forest—even the merchants who had before been willing to supply their needs now made a concerted effort to collect their accounts. It could not be that they feared the Sisters would not pay; when money was lacking because pupil accounts were in arrears, Mother Theodore exchanged the meager supplies on hand for more urgent necessities.

"I am afraid the people have been turned against us," she admitted to Sister St. Francis Xavier, whose quick sympathy made her an easy confidante.

"Poor Mother! I wish I knew a way to help. We shall not have food for the few pupils we have, and if we send them away, how shall we accomplish the work we have come for?"

"It is God's work, too, we must remember, Sister. He will not abandon us if only we can trust Him enough. There is still one merchant in Terre Haute who has been most obliging to us. Of course, we have been paying him regularly. Please God, with the good harvest we shall have, we can continue to do so!"

Mother Theodore and her little household were counting heavily on the expected harvest, which now at the end of September was being gathered into the barn and made ready for the fall and winter. "I have sent to town for what we need right now," she went on. "Can this be the boy back so soon?"

But the young man who stood twisting his cap in the doorway had most unpleasant news. As she reached for the envelope which with some embarrassment he tendered her, Mother Theodore felt a sudden little tremor of apprehension.

She opened the message slowly, and read with wondering disbelief.

"Mother, what is it?" cried Sister St. Francis.

[ 65 ]

"Oh, it cannot be! He demands full payment now, as he wishes to close out our account."

"Close our account? Oh, Mother!"

"From now on, he says, we can buy only for cash!"

For cash! Where was it to come from? "We have a hundred and fifty bushels of wheat in the barn," Mother Theodore said. "Oh, Sister, pray! You do that the best, you know. All I can think to do right now is to write to the bishop for some sort of assurance for this good merchant. Perhaps he will be persuaded to extend our credit a little while."

It was a busy and harried week end. Saturday, ushering in once more the magical, golden month of October, found everyone occupied in helping to garner the last of the hay and corn for the stock. Sunday, the feast of the Holy Angels and Mother Theodore's birthday, was a beautiful sunny day. It was with a sense of work well done and confidence well placed that the foundress went to her room after dinner.

A novice had scarcely joined her there when the two were startled by an uncommon din. Cries and running footsteps shattered the Sunday quiet.

"Fire!" cried an excited postulant. "Fire! Oh, Mother, Sisters! We are on fire!"

It was true. As Mother Theodore later described the sight which met their horrified gaze, "In less than three minutes the two buildings containing our wagons, plows, and all the farm implements constituted an immense oven from which a bright and circling flame rose to a prodigious height and threw to a great distance a shower of sparks. Carried by the brisk, though not high wind, the sparks kindled fires all around, making the first one still more terrible. The green trees beginning to turn caught fire as well as those which were dry."

And of course the barn caught fire. With no water except the scanty supply from a small stream in the ravine, they had to watch the labors of spring and summer and the hopes for fall and winter vanish in a few moments. All they could hope to do was to prevent the spread of the flames to the convent itself and to the stable and fences. "Everything was on fire. Nothing could be seen but fire, and sparks fell upon us, particularly from the trees. The men were there working at top speed. We had them cut down those trees which though the most beautiful were the most dangerous because of their height. They took their axes and hewed away with all their might in this species of purgatory. Some half-consumed pieces of wood fell around them and immediately fire broke out in the clothes of one, in the hair of another, and in the hat of a third. Almost all of us have burns, but by a special Providence, no one has been seriously hurt."

Through the night the Sisters, the workmen, the neighbors labored to quench the flames and to prevent their spread. It was a night of terrible anxiety. A rising wind might cause a forest fire or shower devastating sparks on the frame convent. It was not until late Monday morning that they could acknowledge the danger over. But all around them ashes, blackened posts, the charred remains of felled trees proclaimed their destitution. Worst of all, they were stunned at first by fear that the fire might have been deliberately caused through hostility towards them and their work. Eagerly they sought for more reassuring causes of the disaster and welcomed the suggestion of carelessness or accident.

Meantime, they still had their creditors to face, now with practically no resources. There remained to them the potatoes and apples which were yet to be gathered; they traded their little gristmill for flour, some calves for forage; the bishop despite his own poverty was able to secure for them some coffee and sugar. Far from their mother house in France, from which they scarcely heard at all, they faced the early, bitter winter of 1842 with only their own devotedness and their trust in Providence to support them. Then one day Mother Theodore called the other Sisters around her. "I can think of only one means of obtaining help," she said. "It is our last resource—a voyage to France, to acquaint our friends there with our plight, and to seek from them the assistance they only can give."

The bishop approved of the plan. In spite of her poor health, and all her concern for the household she was leaving, she set out on the long trip late in April with the American novice, Sister Mary Cecilia Bailly.

As Sister St. Francis remarked, "There are some terrible *musts* in this life!"

## Two Beggars and a Queen

**13** Sunbeams slanting through the window of the chancery in Paris danced on a great glass paperweight in the center of the polished desk. Behind the desk, Monsieur the Keeper of the Seals balanced his slender quill and smiled kindly at his visitors.

"You must write to the queen!" he said.

"Write to the queen!" Sister Mary Cecilia gasped.

"Yes," he repeated. "You must write to Her Majesty. I myself will deliver your letter." He placed a chair near his desk, set out stationery, and, dipping his quill in ink, offered it graciously to Mother Theodore, who obediently seated herself and began with great care to compose a suitable little note to Queen Amelia.

"Just ask her for an audience," he advised. "You have every reason to hope. Queen Amelia has the most tender heart imaginable."

"Do you think the queen will really see us?" whispered Sister Mary Cecilia as they left the office a few moments later.

"I feel confident that she will. This is the answer to our prayers at the church of Our Lady of Victories this morning, when Father Desgenettes affiliated our Congregation to the Archconfraternity of the Immaculate Heart. You see, Our Lady is already showing her motherly interest!"

Mother Theodore's thoughts raced back through the months since they had arrived in France—heartbreaking, discouraging months, months of pleading that had brought so little return. It was not that the people of France were not generous and interested in the missions; the very opposite was true. The Society for the Propagation of the Faith had been founded in France. But recent economic losses had crippled many parts of the country. Besides, just at this summer season those who still had the means to help were away from their homes. So, although friendly priests preached eloquent sermons, there was scarcely any response. It was beginning to look as though the Sisters would return home poorer if possible than when they had left, if indeed they could return at all; for they had not even enough money for passage.

As they left the church of Our Lady of Victories, resigned to giving up their quest, Sister Mary Cecilia had once more begged her superior to present the one letter which remained to them. It was addressed to Mlle. Lebrouche at the chancery. Time and again they had passed this building, reluctant to enter a place frequented by the Ministers of State.

"Please, Mother!" urged Sister Mary Cecilia.

"Well, to please you, then, Sister, I will try."

It was well that she did. Mlle. Lebrouche, they learned, was governess to the daughter of the Keeper of the Seals and Minister of Worship, Monsieur Martin du Nord. Gracious and sympathetic, she promised to obtain for them an interview with her employer. And now he himself was on his way to the queen with their request for an audience!

A week later, the superior at the Visitation Convent, where the Sisters were staying, smilingly handed Mother Theodore a letter arrived by courier. It was from the queen herself, Marie-Amélie de Bourbon. She would meet them at the Tuileries at one o'clock next day, October 2.

Queen Amelia did not keep her guests waiting. A moment after they entered her apartment she appeared, tall, graceful, dignified, and motherly. "You must sit down," she said kindly, "here, by me." She herself disposed the chairs and drew her own close to theirs. "Now," she continued, "tell me all about your work."

She was interested in every detail and captivated Sister Mary Cecilia by speaking to her in English. "And now what can I do to help you?" she asked, when their eager recital had ended.

"As a favor, Your Majesty, we ask that you pay our passage back to America."

Without a moment's hesitation, Queen Amelia answered, "It shall be paid. But that is not enough. You will want something for yourselves when you are back in your woods. I myself will solicit for you, and have the king and my children contribute." Queen Amelia was the daughter of the Bourbon King of the Sicilies, the granddaughter of Empress Maria Theresa, and the niece of Queen Marie Antoinette. She had married Louis Philippe of the House of Orleans who had become king of the French in 1830. The mother of eight children, Queen Amelia led a simple, devoted life caring for her family and helping the needy. She spent most of her large fortune in good works.

The missionaries were overwhelmed by her sincere generosity and genuine interest in their work. "Let us save souls, my Sisters," she exhorted them. "That is all that matters here below!"

"Ah, how true that is, Mother!" exclaimed Mother Theodore. And then she caught herself. She had called Her Majesty "Mother"!

"Oh, I am so sorry!" she apologized quickly.

"No, that is quite all right," returned the queen. "You must call me 'Mother.' It is a name that is very dear to me. But here is the king."

The two Sisters turned, to find King Louis Philippe bowing in the plush-draped doorway. The "Citizen King" was very cordial and friendly to them. "You must show our guests the chapel," he directed the queen, after the visitors had been duly presented. So all went to the royal chapel, where the king pointed out, among other things, the queen's confessional.

"And yours, Sire?" asked Sister Mary Cecilia.

He laughed as they passed on. King Louis Philippe felt, like many Frenchmen of his day, that religion was something to be taken care of by the women of the house. And his queen took care of it admirably.

Before they left the palace, the Sisters visited also with Madame Adelaide, the king's sister. When they went out into the October sunshine it was with light hearts and rekindled spirits.

This visit marked a turning point in their mission to France. Soon a sermon preached by Bishop Forbin-Janson brought them two thousand francs. Other bishops, following the queen's example, gave permission for collections to be made. Two zealous journalists whom Mother Theodore had met at Tours, Léon Aubineau and Louis Veuillot, of the *Univers*, were circulating an account of her mission. Those who could not give money were generous in offering prayers, so that at last with relief Mother Theodore could write, "So many prayers are being offered that I doubt not that God will bless this little Congregation."

She was growing more and more anxious to return to her Congregation in the Woods, but her friends were begging her to remain a while. "You must not think of returning to America yet," they urged. "Everyone is becoming interested now; vacationers will soon be home. You will be well advised to prolong your stay."

But the disturbing reports which were reaching Mother Theodore from across the sea made her question this advice. Things were not all going well at St. Mary's. It seemed that the visits of the bishop left behind them worry and distress. His Excellency wanted to make changes in both rules and personnel which the Sisters felt would be disastrous. Then, too, some of the French Sisters were finding almost too hard to bear the decision that the community in America be separated from that of Ruillé. There was the poverty, too, that Mother knew prevailed. The Sisters might hide from her their privations, but their loneliness and their fears they could not keep entirely out of their letters, and she feared that her absence had already been too much prolonged.

Mother Mary shared her concern. "Hurry home, Sister Theodore," she told her, "where you are so badly needed. All the gold in France will not make up for what your mission will lose if you do not hurry back to your Sisters now!"

## Good Saint Anne!

**14** Two new postulants accompanied Mother Theodore and Sister Mary Cecilia on the return voyage aboard the *Nashville*. Sister Mary Cecilia could scarcely suppress her joy at being once more homeward-bound; the two young girls looked with eager anticipation towards a world completely new to them; as for Mother Theodore, she, too, felt that now she was going home, for now America, instead of France, was home to her.

At Havre a surprise awaited the travelers. Not only had the queen paid their passage, but she sent them a basket of refreshments from her own table, and an oil painting of herself, as a souvenir of the enchanted hour when they had discussed, in the palace of the queen, the affairs of their King. And her interest was to follow them to America. A year later they received through the French Embassy an offering of fifteen hundred dollars from Queen Amelia for their missionary work.

Now as the vessel struggled through unruly seas, Mother Theodore took grateful stock of their journey. Besides the kindness of Her Majesty, it had brought other consolations. There was the opportunity to discuss American problems with Mother Mary at Ruillé; to visit "Little Providence" and the woods where in his declining years their founder had loved to sit reading his breviary and praying for the Brothers and Sisters now carrying on his projects for God's glory. There was a visit to her own sister Marie-Jeanne, and to the family of Sister St. Francis at Saint-Servan. At Soulaines Father Brillouet, Monsieur de la Bertaudière, and other friends had proudly shown her their nowcompleted church.

She had arranged for the handling of any funds realized from their quest, and had made many purchases for her Sisters at home. In their trunks were the "black and white yarn for knitting, worsted for tapestry, twist silk in skeins," that Sister Basilide had asked her to procure for the pupils, together with the accessories for making flowers, the sabots, and even the piano strings. There were gifts, too, from devoted friends for the chapel, and needed articles of clothing. The voyage had not been in vain; but as the *Nashville* launched out into the stormy winter seas, Mother Theodore suffered from a sense of foreboding intensified by the perils all around them. What would she find when she returned to Indiana? Or would they ever see it again?

Indeed, for days and nights on end it seemed that they would never reach America. One terrible storm continued unabated for an entire week.

"I've weathered storms in my day," declared a veteran sailor, "but never the like of this!"

"You may well say that! In my thirty-seven and a

[ 73 ]

half years at sea I have never seen such a tempest!"

As the seamen spoke, the waves breaking over the ship swept them back from the rail. The vessel tossed about like an empty shell; eventually everything movable on deck was carried into the churning sea. In the continued blackness the squeals of animals as they were washed overboard were lost amid the crash of waves and the shrieks of passengers half-demented with fright. Those in the steerage lost everything they had, even their cooking utensils. One morning the Sisters watched while the body of a child of eight, who had died during the night, was lowered into the sea.

Night after night the Sisters passed the dark, sleepless hours making the Way of the Cross, and one by one their frightened shipmates joined them, none of them knowing at what moment all would be lost together. Among the earnest promises the Sisters made, Mother Theodore, true to her Breton traditions, pledged herself to build a shrine and institute a pilgrimage in honor of St. Anne if the ship should be spared. Just before Christmas the climax was reached. A devastating gale from the southwest heightened the wave of destruction. What boats remained were cut adrift; the wind-driven fury of the storm was insatiable.

There was no thought of sleep for anyone that night. In the Sisters' cabin, prayers were redoubled. Finally, about three o'clock in the morning, the inevitable seemed to have arrived. Water thundered through every porthole; the tops of the masts disappeared into the sea; the vessel had completely capsized. There was no apparent hope.

"Good Saint Anne," cried Mother Theodore, "pray for us now!" The cry was taken up by those near her. "Good Saint Anne," they repeated, scarcely knowing what they said.

And suddenly the wind, veering to the north, flung up a huge wave which righted the sinking ship. Frenzied cries for mercy turned to sobs of incredulous gratitude. The captain, even *his* burly frame trembling with relief, exclaimed in awe, "That was quick as lightning! We were gone! I was sure we were gone!"

"Good Saint Anne!" repeated the Sisters. Then and there they renewed the resolution which was to result in the erection of the Chapel of St. Anne and the pilgrimage in her honor held at St. Mary's annually for over a hundred years.

Meantime, the captain directed his battered vessel southward out of disabling currents. They were nearing the West Indies, and Mother Theodore's thoughts were hastening ahead to New Orleans and the journey's end, when a hideous shriek startled her from her reverie. The next second Sister Mary Cecilia was beside her. "Oh, Mother, they are going to kill each other!"

"They" were the captain and a refractory seaman he was trying to subdue. Unable to withdraw, the Sisters watched in horror as the struggling men passed them. At last with a powerful blow the captain mastered his opponent and thrust him into the hold. A sailor fastened the trapdoor, and the captain turned, flushed and gasping, only to drop like a felled tree to the deck.

All eyes turned to the scene. "He is dying!" "It is a stroke!" "What shall we do?" "What will become of us?" Accustomed to look to Mother Theodore for a solution in every emergency, Sister Mary Cecilia turned to her superior.

"Let us see what we can do," Mother Theodore said quietly, approaching the group gathered around the captain. The rough sailors moved aside with awkward respect as she bent over the stricken man. "He should be bled," she said. All hurried to carry out her directions, and she herself proceeded with the operation. Respect for her deepened when in a few moments the captain opened his eyes. A short time later he was back at his duties.

"He overexerted himself," Mother Theodore said

softly to Sister Mary Cecilia. "Thank God he has recovered. What would the ship do without the captain?"

Even with the captain's skillful management, the voyage still continued to be a singularly dangerous venture. It was not until January 27, after eight weeks at sea, that they disembarked at New Orleans, where the Sisters found hospitality in the Ursuline Convent. There the very next morning Mother Theodore was stricken with an illness which was to keep her from Indiana for seven more weeks.

"I always find a new sacrifice to make when I think I have reached the end," she wrote to Mother Mary. "May God be blest for it! In eternity it will not be too much!"

As soon as her fever permitted, she turned to Sister Mary Cecilia, who hovered close to her bed. "You must go on ahead, Sister," she said, "and take the postulants. The Sisters at home must not be kept in suspense any longer."

"But, Mother, it is you they wish to see. How can I face them without you?"

"They will have to make do with you." Mother Theodore smiled with a wan touch of her old gaiety. "They won't turn you away, I am sure. And you can tell them all my news."

As Sister Mary Cecilia feared, the Sisters were bitterly disappointed when she returned without Mother Theodore. "I had to go around and ask them to welcome me," she wrote to New Orleans. "They ask me, 'Why didn't you bring Mother?' Oh, Mother, do come! Your presence is needed in a most distressing manner. Come as soon as you can travel!"

It was not, however, until the end of March that Mother Theodore could start the journey north. The lamplighters were beginning their rounds in the dusky streets of Vincennes as she alighted outside the convent, a little yellow house in which the bishop had established Sisters during her absence. The Sisters were reciting their evening rosary; as Sister Stanislaus left chapel to prepare supper, she glanced briefly towards the window, then, dropping her apron, ran to fling open the door.

"Mother!"

In a moment the traveler was surrounded by Sisters smiling through their tears, though the tears threatened to predominate as they noted her emaciation. For her part, Mother Theodore noticed at once the real penury in which the Vincennes Sisters lived. With neither glass nor table napkin to set at her place, they shared with her their small portions of corned beef, as they listened to her and just looked at her.

The Mother's penetrating gaze had noted something else—the air of distress and preoccupation which Sister Superior could not entirely hide. "Now, Sister St. Vincent," she began as soon as the other Sisters had withdrawn, "you have something to tell me. What is it that worries you?"

"It is for you that I grieve, Mother, and for the Sisters at St. Mary's, who are so longing to see you again. Mother, you *will* go to St. Mary's for a time at least, in order to console them?"

"What can you mean, Sister? Of course I am going to St. Mary's as soon as I have paid my respects to our bishop and arranged my transportation."

"Oh, Mother, I am so relieved! I have been praying that you would!"

"I am afraid I do not understand you, Sister. Why should I not go to St. Mary's? Why should you have to pray that I would? Sister, please explain this mystery!"

"But, Mother, you know—surely you know—that Monseigneur has forbidden you to return to St. Mary's?"

# Beneath the Cross

**15** "Yes, Mother," repeated Sister St. Vincent, "Monseigneur has said over and over that he will not permit you to go back to St. Mary's. We could only hope and pray and suffer. You can imagine how we felt when Sister Mary Cecilia came back alone. We were sure that we should never see you again! We could scarcely welcome the poor dear!"

"Now I begin to understand her letter, Sister. But now, you see, I am here, and surely Monseigneur will not forbid me to go on to St. Mary's!"

"I am afraid he will. He is very angry with you, Mother. Unless you can prevail upon him to change his mind, it looks as though our community will be lost."

"Confidence, Sister St. Vincent! In any case I would be calling on Monseigneur in the morning. Let us pray earnestly at Mass, and marshal all our courage to meet him."

It took, indeed, a great deal of courage to face the indignant prelate. At first he refused even to acknowledge the presence of the two Sisters. Then he turned to Mother Theodore, who, still weak and ill and worn out after the sleepless night, could scarcely believe what she heard.

"So," he charged, "you have been to consult with your superiors in France in order to find ways of undermining the authority of your bishop!"

"But, Monseigneur, it was with your permission that I went to France, and my purpose, which you approved, was to solicit help."

"Help! And have I not impoverished myself to give you help? Is this the gratitude I receive? But I should not have expected better sentiments, seeing that you have been listening to counselors unfavorable to me!"

It was in vain that Mother Theodore tried to convince him of her continued respect for him and her desire to carry out his wishes as far as she possibly could. "Indeed," she added, "these are the sentiments of all our Sisters."

"That may be true of Sister Basilide, but that other proud little thing must not have anything further to do with our affairs. It is she who has written against me to you, to your superiors in France, and to the Bishop of Le Mans—who besides has nothing to say in my diocese!"

"I am sure, Your Excellency," said Mother Theodore, "that Sister St. Francis Xavier has no desire of prejudicing anyone against you. She desires only peace and the success of God's work."

"Do not speak to me of her. Let us come back to you. I demand the money that you stole from me in France."

"Stole, Monseigneur?"

"You obtained there money which was destined for my diocese, for which I have other purposes than those to which you will put it."

"But, Monseigneur, the money which was assigned to me in France by the Propagation of the Faith was only that set aside for our establishment; it in no way reduced what you are to receive for your other needs."

"There is no need to try to deceive me. I am well informed, about that and about what you were doing in New Orleans, where you stayed behind for your own purposes while pretending to be ill."

It was useless for Mother Theodore to try to answer these and the other charges which for two hours Monseigneur hurled at her, all mistaken, and all doubly painful to her because they issued from one whom she respected and revered, one who had sacrificed so much and was so filled with zeal and good intentions.

"You may leave now," he concluded abruptly. "I have other appointments. But return in the morning. I have not finished what I have to say to you."

As may well be imagined, Mother Theodore passed the rest of that day and the following night in anxiety and prayer. When she returned to the bishop's house, she found him in somewhat better dispositions. He had received a letter from the chaplain at St. Mary's, Father Corbé; besides, he could not deny his own observations that Mother Theodore was truly weak and ill.

She was quick to note and shrewdly pursue the advantage which the slight improvement in his manner offered. "I may return to my Sisters?" she asked. "May I write to tell them I am coming?" And because she knew it pleased him to be asked to bestow his blessing, which she sincerely desired for herself and her Sisters, she added, "You will send them your blessing?"

She had judged correctly.

"Yes," he replied, "you may write them. Sit down here now and write, and send them their bishop's blessing."

Mother Theodore hurried to comply. There was nothing, she knew, that would bring more happiness to the Sisters at St. Mary's in their present fears than to know that she was returning to them with Monseigneur's blessing.

She began immediately the two-day journey from Vincennes to St. Mary-of-the-Woods. Among her Sisters again, she learned at last the details of their suffering during her long absence, because of the bishop's resentment of their loyalty to her. She was prompt to console and encourage them, and to excuse the one Sister among them whose disloyalty and indiscretion had contributed to the community's troubles.

Now she could relieve their poverty, too, with the alms from France, pay back friends who had trusted them, recompense the workmen who had waited months for their wages. All seemed well again, now that the Mother was home, and the bishop only too eager to apologize for his injustice to her.

But the respite was only temporary. During the ensuing three years the tension was always present. While Bishop de la Hailandière often protested that he respected their rules and wished them observed, while he repeatedly stated that he knew no one more capable of directing a religious community than Mother Theodore, he acted in a manner which belied these sentiments. In his letters, in conversations with priests and people, he openly expressed displeasure with the Sisters, especially Mother Theodore. The distress this attitude caused her was her heaviest cross. Sister St. Francis, who had endured the most during her Superior's absence, understood her trial now.

"You could never understand what Sister Theodore has had to suffer," she wrote. "All the illness and fatigues of her voyage are nothing in comparison with her anxieties of conscience. I would prefer death, if it were the will of God, to such a life."

In October of 1844 Monseigneur sent orders that she was not to visit the missions. What was she to do? This was part of her duty, according to the Rule, and more necessary since in some schools there were very young Sisters, still untrained, placed in responsible positions by the bishop himself during her absence. Their duties were almost incredibly strenuous: they rose before five for prayer and study before a school day which lasted until four-thirty. After school there were the household duties, the cow to milk, the supper to cook, the morrow's lessons to prepare. As for their living conditions—"a bowl of milk and a piece of bread make a delicious meal," wrote Sister St. Liguori from St. Peter's. Again, "There was snow on our table, from three openings between the logs." At Vincennes the Sisters slept for weeks on the floor, and the rain came through the roof of their kitchen, whose broken windows did not admit enough light to see the utensils properly. These harsh conditions, endured joyfully by the Sisters, were having a terrifying effect on their health.

At the mother house, there was need of building a permanent convent and enlarging the school; but the Sisters hesitated to build on land that did not belong to them, and the bishop continually put off fulfilling his promise to give the woodland property to the community.

More than once, after prayer and sacrifice, Mother Theodore took her courage in hand and tried to placate their bishop, whom they still revered and respected, knowing well that he had many problems to face and that his temperament added difficulties to his already heavy task.

"We only desire, Monseigneur," she told him on one occasion, "to do all we can to ease the hardships of our position here. If we continue under your displeasure, our work is bound to suffer. It would be better for us to leave the diocese than remain to be a source of scandal."

The bishop drew himself up to his imperious height. "That is not for you to decide," he declared. "This community belongs to me, not to you. If you do not find yourself satisfied, you may leave." He made a gesture embracing the forest and its frame and log buildings. "I am the proprietor here. I can forbid you to set foot in that house again."

And that is just what he did when Mother Theodore, on a visit to Vincennes in May of 1847, made still another effort to plead with him. Twice he refused to admit her. Then he received her haughtily and, after subjecting her to all the facets of his anger, finally pronounced, "I forbid you to return to St. Mary's. I deprive you of all your rights of superiorship. I dispense you from your vows while you are in Indiana, and I forbid you to have, even by letter, any communication with the Sisters of Providence at St. Mary-of-the-Woods." He turned on his heel and left the room and his astonished visitor.

Completely crushed, she returned to the little yellow convent and tried to make some plans for the future. To Sister St. Vincent she gave the keys and money she had with her, and she asked Sister Mary Xavier to go the next day to inform the Sisters at St. Mary's and Father Corbé of the bishop's sentence. Where she herself would go, she did not know; but it must be alone, for the bishop had declared that any Sister who followed her from the diocese would be excommunicated.

By the following morning, grief and anxiety, together with a heavy cold she had been fighting for over a month, conspired to reduce her to a state of critical illness. She was forced, then, to remain in a house where the Sisters felt in danger of excommunication for keeping her, and the priest whom they sent for did not come. It seemed to her that at last God was offering her the ultimate privilege of sharing His own Cross, as, rejected and abandoned, she seemed about to die. But I shall be happy to die, she thought, for thus the community can be saved.

## Season of Sowing

**16** While Mother Theodore, in Vincennes, touched the limit of her three-year trial, the Sisters at St. Mary's were experiencing also the utmost distress. There was no need to question Sister Mary Xavier, when she arrived alone; one look at her wan and tearful face told them that their worst fears had been realized. She nodded assent to their unspoken queries.

"It has come to pass. Our Mother has been deposed, forbidden to return to us—and besides, she is ill, ill enough to die! And she feels herself a burden in the Vincennes house, where the Sisters dread Monseigneur's censures if they keep her."

Father Corbé had further bad news to add. "The bishop has written me," he told them, "that we are to hold an election to choose a new Mother General, now that Mother Theodore has been forbidden to return. You know how I feel about this. However, we must see what the community thinks."

The unanimous decision of the community was to retain their Mother. They would be faithful to her, they declared, whatever might happen. Not to be outdone, the workmen also announced their intention to follow Mother Theodore and the Sisters into whatever new home they might find if driven from the diocese. Jean Delahaye, the gardener, saddled his horse and started off immediately to Vincennes with a consoling letter to Mother Theodore, and the Sisters began a campaign of prayer and penance to procure the end of their trials. Father Corbé made a hurried trip by night to Vincennes to bring the Last Sacraments to the patient; Sister Olympiade was sent to nurse her, and Sister Mary Cecilia hastened to be near her.

She was not yet convalescent when the news came that was finally to mark the beginning of the end of their sorrows. First there were rumors that Monseigneur de la Hailandière was resigning his see. The rumors gained substance when reliable information supplied the name of his successor, the Very Reverend John Stephen Bazin, Vicar-General of Mobile. Then Monseigneur de la Hailandière, realizing that his resignation had been accepted, renounced his authority over the Sisters of Providence. Mother Theodore was free to return to her Sisters.

She reached St. Mary's at sunset on a beautiful June evening, to be greeted royally, with a salute of cannon at Terre Haute, a volley of gunshots at the entrance to the Woods, and a joyful procession, headed by Father Lalumière on horseback, and closed by the pupils and the little dog Taillard. Father Corbé waited in the chapel, where all gathered for Benediction and fervent prayers of thanksgiving.

The new bishop was all that their harassed souls could desire. "Bury the past in forgetfulness," he wrote to Mother Theodore, "and never think of it save to bless the Providence of God which sent you crosses out of love, for He never fails to afflict His true children."

One of his first projects was to move the Sisters in Vincennes to a more suitable building near the cathedral; and he himself helped to make the transfer, just in time to escape the first heavy snowfall. The new house afforded the Sisters room to open the dispensary which the bishop desired; so early in the spring Mother Theodore arrived with a generous store of Sister Olympiade's herbs and remedies to stock the pharmacy, and the capable Sister Joachim to minister to the sick poor. Monseigneur Bazin was very well pleased, and Mother Theodore's feeling of relief and encouragement increased, as it did each time she saw or heard from him.

It was a shock to her, then, to find when she returned to Vincennes in Passion Week, that the new bishop was seriously ill. In spite of a heavy cold, he had been working at the orphanage during the week, and had spent many hours on Saturday in the confessional. On Palm Sunday he was confined to bed with fever; by Holy Thursday Mother Theodore, alarmed at his condition, was devoting her knowledge and experience in medicine to assist the doctor who attended him. All their efforts were futile.

"I have no more hope of saving him," she wrote sadly to the Sisters on Holy Thursday. "How devout and edifying he is. . . . He spoke to me of you all, for his thoughts are upon our Congregation."

Towards evening on Saturday it was evident to all that the bishop was dying. The priests and Sisters of Vincennes gathered at his bedside while he ad-

[ 85 ]

dressed them words of blessing and encouragement until his strength failed completely. Mother Theodore remained throughout the night, trying to ease his last moments. "Tell your Sisters that if I had lived I would have tried to do much for them," he said to her. He died shortly after sunrise on Easter Sunday morning.

"Our loss is immense," wrote Mother Theodore to the Sisters, "but we must not be discouraged. Let us submit to the will of God. He has always protected us; if we love Him, He will never abandon us."

Their confidence was justified when, a few months later, Bishop James Maurice de Saint-Palais was appointed Bishop of Vincennes. He was to have a long administration, and by his wisdom and benevolence, energy and devotion, help the Sisters to build firmly on the foundations that had been laid in the shadow of the Cross.

During those years of trial the work at St. Mary-of-the-Woods had been blessed in many ways. The enrollment had increased so much that it became necessary to enlarge the school building. More important, the non-Catholic pupils were beginning to show an interest in the faith; frequently feast days were celebrated with ceremonies of baptism or First Communion.

As the reputation of St. Mary's Institute grew, other places begged for Sisters. Besides Jasper, there were now schools in Madison, St. Peter's, Vincennes, Fort Wayne, and Terre Haute. Bishops in other dioceses, too, including their good friend Bishop Martin in Louisiana, repeatedly asked Mother Theodore to send them Sisters. It was a grief to her that she could not accede to all their requests, but the schools already established had to be adequately staffed first. Mother Theodore had reason to be pleased with the work of her Sisters wherever they were.

At St. Mary's they were able in 1852, with the encouragement and assistance of Bishop de Saint-

Palais, to replace the old Thralls farmhouse with a brick mother house. The Institute, as a center of culture, was rapidly becoming an Indiana tradition. American girls of the mid-nineteenth century tried hard to copy the gracious manners and the gentle distinction of their teachers and enjoyed to the full the years they spent in acquiring these graces. Booth Tarkington, Indiana novelist, described those early days when he said of his mother's education at St. Mary-of-the-Woods, "Something rare and fine was brought from France to Saint Mary-of-the-Woods, and none of those who were taught there remained unaffected by it." "Although my mother rarely spoke of this," he continued, "more often dwelling on her affection for the Sisters and the beauty of the place itself, the manner of Saint Mary-of-the-Woods springs to my mind whenever I delve for the true meaning of 'lady.' "

Mother Theodore could be content, then, that she was laying a good foundation for a splendid work. She was content, too, with the companions whom God had sent to work with her. There was first the fervent Irma Le Fer, Sister St. Francis Xavier, her trusted confidante and zealous assistant. In spite of her delicate health, Sister St. Francis worked untiringly in guiding the novices, teaching the catechism, assisting with the work of the Propagation of the Faith, spreading good literature, and everything else that her devoted and prayerful heart could devise.

There was Irma's sister Elvire, now Sister Mary Joseph, charming and talented, teaching the novices and students music and French. Elvire loved to accompany Sister Olympiade on her visits of charity to the village, and nothing delighted her more than being able, on occasion, to baptize some infant in danger of death, or to bring relief to an ailing child. She gave promise of being a treasure to the community as she progressed.

There were Sister Mary Cecilia and Sister St.

Urbain, and so many other dedicated, scholarly, distinguished teachers; there were so many promising postulants. Mother Theodore could well feel that her work was becoming firmly established.

She was commenting on their blessings and expressing her gratitude as she and Sister St. Francis returned one evening from a business trip to Terre Haute. She had taken Sister as companion to give her a little outing, for Sister St. Francis Xavier's health never left her superior free from concern.

"I declare to you, Sister," she teased, "if you are well one day you do penance for it by being ill the next three. Now that you are feeling like yourself again, do come with me to town, please."

It was a long trip to town in those days, but the hours they spent jogging along in the wagon gave them time to exchange their views, to reminisce, and to share their sentiments of trust in Providence. "Do you know, Mother," said Sister St. Francis, "I wish you had let me pray for an instantaneous cure that last time I was ill. I am so sure that Our Lady would have obtained it for me! And then think how we could have praised her!"

Mother Theodore was silent for a moment. "I don't doubt it, Sister. I am sure Our Lady would have answered your prayer, but I was afraid I would not be able to stand the happiness all at once. And she did restore you to us, even though she did it gradually. I am grateful for that. Besides, we can still praise her. I often think that everything we have obtained here in the forest has come through her hands. She seems to be watching over us. I am so glad you have inaugurated the sodality!"

"The girls are enthusiastic, Mother, especially since the promulgation of the dogma of the Immaculate Conception!"

"The Immaculate Conception! She is the patroness of America, and ours, too! When we have a church here at St. Mary-of-the-Woods, it shall be called in her honor. Meantime, Sister, it is time to be saying her Office. Let us offer vespers today in thanksgiving for all God's wonderful care of us!"

The two rode along quietly then, reading their psalms, as the evening darkened and moonbeams began to sprinkle an air of enchantment over the forest around them. It was just as they reached the verse, "Out of the depths I have cried to Thee, O Lord," that Sister St. Francis became aware of the backing of the horse. They were on a narrow, unrailed bridge, beneath which yawned a deep ravine; as the horse moved, the wheels of the carriage moved, too, to within an inch of the edge. Automatically Sister St. Francis jumped from the carriage, calling to Mother Theodore to do the same. But it was too late. With one quick, terrible crash, horse and carriage had plunged over the edge, dragging the foundress with them.

Terrified, Sister St. Francis fairly flew down the rocky declivity to where the poor Mother lay wedged in between the carriage wheels in such a way that one movement of the horse's legs might have killed her. At that moment, in answer to Sister's cries, a young man appeared on the bridge, and leaving his wagon, sped to the rescue. With his help Mother Theodore was gently released, the horse righted, and only the wrecked carriage remained to testify to the danger from which they had been snatched.

In her excitement, Sister St. Francis expressed her thanks in French to their bewildered young rescuer, who found her effusions quite unintelligible.

"You had a very narrow escape," he stammered, looking with a puzzled air from the splintered carriage to the plank bridge above. "That was quite a fall!" Still shaking his head, he went back to his wagon, promising to send them further help.

Sister St. Francis was busy whispering prayers of gratitude. As for Mother Theodore, she rose and walked calmly up the incline, apparently none the worse for her adventure except for a few bruises. But she and her Sisters had still another instance of God's protection to ponder.

## *"Eternity!"*

**17** Often, as a girl, Anne-Thérèse Guérin had pondered the magical word "eternity." It had been the subject of her meditations many times during her religious life; during her sixteen years in America, especially, she had come to view many things in its light. Many times, too, she had come close to stepping over its borders.

As the bitter winter of 1855 progressed, a winter so cold that the wine froze in the chalice at Mass in the village church, the conviction grew in her that her eternity was drawing near. Always delicate, for years she had been forced to keep almost a perpetual fast; of late she had been bothered by a persistent cough and troublesome pains in her chest. She succumbed easily to the colds prevalent in the cruel winters and to the fevers which were periodically epidemic. It was a marvel to others, indeed, that she continued to work as she did. Always available to the Sisters and to the workmen, carrying on a large correspondence, overseeing the work of building and farm as well as visiting the various schools, she did not spare herself, although at last she was obliged to admit, "I am truly tired," adding at once, "but I shall rest, I feel, only in heaven."

The Sisters noticed her condition, too, and what they would do without her they did not dare to think, for they had depended on her from the beginning. The French Sisters who had accompanied her to the New World could not imagine themselves without her leadership. Each of the Americans she had received and cared for like a true mother. "She loves us so much!" wrote one of her novices, "that one is driven to think, 'Our Mother would give her life for me!'"

During her many serious illnesses over the years, the community literally stormed heaven with prayer and sacrifice, and always their prayers were heard. This, they sometimes half-jokingly said, was because Sister St. Francis Xavier led their celestial assaults, being determined not to let Mother Theodore die while she herself was still alive.

Toward the end of January, 1856, however, Sister St. Francis suddenly became very ill. Noting her high fever and her delirium, Mother Theodore was alarmed.

On the morning of January 28, she stopped Sister Mary Joseph after Mass. "I find Sister St. Francis very ill," she said. "Pray hard and ask the novices to pray. I am afraid she will not recover."

All that day the novices took turns reciting the rosary. In the intervals, Sister Mary Joseph sat at her sister's bedside, listening to her fervent aspirations and thinking to herself, "Now I shall find out how you make your meditations, and perhaps learn to love God as you do!" And all day the invalid tossed in delirium. In one of her quiet moments she tried to convey to Mother Theodore the sentiments that were filling her heart.

"I shall go to heaven forever," she whispered. "Oh, Mother, together we shall enjoy God during all eternity!"

On Thursday, January 31, with all the community gathered about her, she died calmly and peacefully, leaving her Sisters to ponder her last words, "Forever, O my God! and for so little! So much happiness for so little!"

Her illness had been so brief, her death, despite her always fragile health, so unexpected, that the community was stunned. For Mother Theodore, her passing left a heartbreaking void.

"She was everything to me," wrote the bereft foundress to Ruillé. "She was a friend that one does not lose twice in a lifetime. Her death leaves me as it were alone in the midst of the community. I did not think, nor did the Sisters, that in my poor state of health I could survive this dear Sister."

It was in a different strain, however, that she tried to be an example of fortitude and resignation to her companions. "My dear Sisters," she urged them, "since we have a sacrifice to make, let us make it generously!" She tried to keep back her own tears, that they might grieve less.

There was truly little time to indulge in sorrow during the next few weeks. With the little strength she could muster, she must write the sad news to the missions and to their friends. Someone must be trained to do Sister's work in the novitiate and the mother house; and the regular work of community and school must go on. All the while her exhaustion was growing; zeal and determination alone kept her at her post. When Sister Olympiade remonstrated with her for attempting to go to chapel, she replied that is was only the Mass which gave her strength through the day.

The Sisters watched in distress as all during February and March she grew daily weaker, her brisk step slower, her very breathing a labor. On Palm Sunday, March 16, the Forty Hours' Devotion opened in the convent chapel, and she joined the Sisters in their hours of adoration. She attempted to hear Mass the following morning also, but had to leave before its end. "I left Mass," she said to Sister Rose. "It is my last!"

"Mother, do not say that! Our Lord must leave you with us a long time yet. We need you!"

"My poor Sister! God will provide. But this is really my last illness, you will see!"

"Now, Mother, we have brought you through attacks just as bad, or worse," chided Sister Olympiade. Father Corbé agreed with her.

And Dr. Baty, called from Vincennes, was inclined to feel the same. He had seen her just as close to death before. "She will be better in a few days," he said.

But Mother Theodore only smiled and wrote in the diary, "I am obliged to remain in bed. What a beautiful week to be on the cross!" On Holy Saturday, Dr. Baty admitted to Sister Mary Joseph that her superior's condition was alarming.

Easter was a day of great suffering. But even then the Sisters could not realize that this was truly Mother Theodore's last illness. She alone seemed to realize it. She appreciated their last efforts to relieve her pain. Her great fear was to be a burden to them. "You would have nothing to suffer if you did not have me," she would say.

Sister Olympiade, always faithful, scarcely left her room, even to obtain a little sleep. The doctors simply could not believe that this time, as on so many other occasions, her nursing and the prayers of the Sisters would not prevail. But all during April she continued to grow worse, and in early May the Sisters wrote to Ruillé, "It is inconceivable how with her poor health she has been able to endure her cruel sufferings. It is painful to see her."

On the margin of this letter, a few days later, the writer hastily added, "Our Mother is dying! The doctor has no more hope. Oh, pray for us!"

"Our Mother is dying!" They were scarcely able to believe the chilling truth. All day, all night, they lingered near her, whenever they could leave their duties. The Sisters at the academy took turns watching over the boarders at night so that some Sisters might always be near the sickroom. "Do not let me die without the sacraments," she had said from time to time. On May 12 it seemed that the time had come. The Sisters gathered around her bed during the ceremony hoped against hope that the anointing would bring restored health as well as spiritual consolation.

During the next day she lingered, still suffering. Finally, at midnight, Sister Mary Cecilia, seated near the bed, looked around at the others.

"The end is near!"

Someone went for Father Corbé. The others drew near the bed. Father Corbé came immediately, to give the absolution and join the Sisters in the prayers for the dying. The end came on the morning of May 14, 1856, quietly, almost imperceptibly.

The following day Bishop de Saint-Palais officiated at her funeral, and the Sisters themselves carried her casket to the cemetery on St. Anne's Hill. Over her grave they set a white cross with the words, "I sleep, but my heart watches over this house which I have founded."